It's another great book from CGP...

GCSE Physics is all about **understanding how science works**.
And not only that — understanding it well enough to be able to **question** what you hear on TV and read in the papers.

But don't panic. This book includes all the **science facts** you need to learn, and shows you how they work in the real world. It even includes a **free** Online Edition you can read on your computer or tablet.

How to get your free Online Edition

Just go to **cgpbooks.co.uk/extras** and enter this code...

3224 8026 3958 9634

By the way, this code only works for one person. If somebody else has used this book before you, they might have already claimed the Online Edition.

CGP — still the best! ☺

Our sole aim here at CGP is to produce the highest quality books — carefully written, immaculately presented and dangerously close to being funny.

Then we work our socks off to get them out to you — at the cheapest possible prices.

Contents

Published by CGP

From original material by Richard Parsons.

Editors:
Ellen Bowness, Helena Hayes, Felicity Inkpen, Edmund Robinson,
Hayley Thompson, Julie Wakeling, Sarah Williams.

Contributors:
Mark A Edwards, Paddy Gannon, Gemma Hallam, Andy Williams.

ISBN: 978 1 84762 630 1

With thanks to Mark A Edwards, Ian Francis, Karen Wells
and Dawn Wright for the proofreading.

With thanks to Jan Greenway for the copyright research.

Pages 20, 38, 69, 70 and 71 contain public sector information published by the Health
and Safety Executive and licensed under the Open Government Licence v1.0.

Image on page 22 courtesy of NASA Ames Research Center.

With thanks to Science Photo Library for permission
to reproduce the photograph used on page 23.

Data used to construct stopping distance diagram on page 58 from the Highway Code.
© Crown Copyright re-produced under the terms of the Click-Use licence.

With thanks to iStockphoto.com for use of the images on page 92.

www.cgpbooks.co.uk

Printed by Elanders Ltd, Newcastle upon Tyne.
Clipart from Corel®

The Scientific Process

You need to know a few things about how the world of science works. First up is the <u>scientific process</u> — how a scientist's <u>mad idea</u> turns into a <u>widely accepted theory</u>.

Scientists Come Up with Hypotheses — Then Test Them

About 500 years ago, we still thought the Solar System looked like this.

1) Scientists try to <u>explain</u> things. Everything.

2) They start by <u>observing</u> something they don't understand — it could be anything, e.g. planets in the sky, a person suffering from an illness, what matter is made of... anything.

3) Then, they come up with a <u>hypothesis</u> — a <u>possible explanation</u> for what they've observed.

4) The next step is to <u>test</u> whether the hypothesis might be <u>right or not</u> — this involves <u>gathering evidence</u> (i.e. <u>data</u> from <u>investigations</u>).

5) To gather evidence the scientist uses the hypothesis to make a <u>prediction</u> — a statement based on the hypothesis that can be <u>tested</u>.

6) If data from experiments or studies <u>backs up the prediction</u>, you're one step closer to figuring out if the hypothesis is true.

Other Scientists Will Test the Hypotheses Too

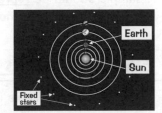

Then we thought it looked like this.

1) <u>Other</u> scientists will use the hypothesis to make their <u>own predictions</u>, and carry out their <u>own experiments</u> or studies.

2) They'll also try to <u>reproduce</u> the original investigations to check the results.

3) And if <u>all the experiments</u> in the world back up the hypothesis, then scientists start to think it's <u>true</u>.

4) However, if a scientist somewhere in the world does an experiment that <u>doesn't</u> fit with the hypothesis (and other scientists can <u>reproduce</u> these results), then the hypothesis is in trouble.

5) When this happens, scientists have to come up with a new hypothesis (maybe a <u>modification</u> of the old hypothesis, or maybe a completely <u>new</u> one).

If Evidence Supports a Hypothesis, It's Accepted — for Now

1) If pretty much every scientist in the world believes a hypothesis to be true because experiments back it up, then it usually goes in the <u>textbooks</u> for students to learn.

2) Accepted hypotheses are often referred to as <u>theories</u>.

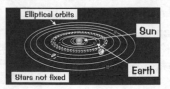

Now we think it's more like this.

3) Our <u>currently accepted</u> theories are the ones that have survived this 'trial by evidence' — they've been tested many, many times over the years and survived (while the less good ones have been ditched).

4) However... they never, <u>never</u> become hard and fast, totally indisputable <u>fact</u>. You can never know... it'd only take <u>one</u> odd, totally inexplicable result, and the hypothesising and testing would start all over again.

You expect me to believe that — then show me the evidence...

Scientific <u>ideas</u> are <u>changing</u> all the time as a result of <u>new evidence</u> being uncovered. It's the role of the scientific community (all the world's scientists) to <u>test</u> and <u>evaluate</u> these ideas and decide whether or not they should be <u>accepted</u> as theories — so you don't have to waste your time learning stuff that's absolute rubbish.

Your Data's Got to Be Good

Evidence is the key to science — but not all evidence is equally good.
The way evidence is gathered can have a big effect on how trustworthy it is...

Lab Experiments and Studies Are Better Than Rumour

1) Results from controlled experiments in laboratories are great. A lab is the easiest place to control variables so that they're all kept constant (except for the one you're investigating). This makes it easier to carry out a fair test.

2) For things that you can't investigate in the lab (e.g. the effect of radiation) you conduct scientific studies. As many of the variables as possible are controlled, to make it a fair test.

3) Old wives' tales, rumours, hearsay, "what someone said", and so on, should be taken with a pinch of salt. Without any evidence they're NOT scientific — they're just opinions.

There's more about variables and fair tests on page 5.

The Bigger the Sample Size the Better

Data based on small samples isn't as good as data based on large samples.
A sample should be representative of the whole population (i.e. it should share as many of the various characteristics in the population as possible) — a small sample can't do that as well.

Evidence Needs to be Reliable (Reproducible)

Evidence is only reliable if other people can repeat it. If they can't, then you can't believe it.

RELIABLE means that the data can be reproduced by others.

EXAMPLE: In 1989, two scientists claimed that they'd produced 'cold fusion' (the energy source of the Sun — but without the enormous temperatures). It was huge news — if true, this could have meant energy from seawater — the ideal energy solution for the world... forever. However, other scientists just couldn't get the same results — i.e. the results weren't reliable. And until they are, 'cold fusion' isn't going to be generally accepted as fact.

Evidence Also Needs to Be Valid

VALID means that the data is reliable AND answers the original question.

EXAMPLE: DO POWER LINES CAUSE CANCER?
Some studies have found that children who live near overhead power lines are more likely to develop cancer. What they'd actually found was a correlation (relationship) between the variables "presence of power lines" and "incidence of cancer" — they found that as one changed, so did the other. But this evidence is not enough to say that the power lines cause cancer, as other explanations might be possible.
For example, power lines are often near busy roads, so the areas tested could contain different levels of pollution from traffic. Also, you need to look at types of neighbourhoods and lifestyles of people living in the tested areas (could diet be a factor... or something else you hadn't thought of...).
So these studies don't show a definite link and so don't answer the original question.

Does the data really say that?...

If it's so hard to be definite about anything, how does anybody ever get convinced about anything?
Well, what usually happens is that you get a load of evidence that all points the same way. If one study can't rule out a particular possibility, then maybe another one can. So you gradually build up a whole body of evidence, and it's this (rather than any single study) that convinces people.

Benefits, Risks and Decision Making

Science is all about the balance between benefit and risk — a bit like life really...

Developments in Science Usually Have Benefits and Drawbacks...

Scientists have created loads of new technologies that could improve our lives.
For example, generating electricity using nuclear power has lots of benefits:

1) The national population benefits from a reliable source of electricity.

2) There's a global benefit because generating electricity this way doesn't contribute to global warming (like coal-fired power stations do).

3) Construction companies benefit from years of work in building the power station.

4) Local people benefit from new jobs.

However, it's not all good news. One of the drawbacks is:

Nuclear power stations are very expensive. Perhaps the money that goes into building them would be better spent on things like building new wind turbines or hydroelectric plants.

...and They're Never Risk Free

1) Most technologies have some risks.
For example, for a new nuclear power station:

- Local people might suffer from higher radiation exposure, which could affect their health.

- There could be a major accident, like the Chernobyl disaster, which would affect large areas.

2) To make a decision about a course of action (e.g. whether or not to build a new nuclear power station) society has to weigh up the benefits, drawbacks and risks involved for everyone.

Loads of Other Factors Can Influence Decisions Too

Here are some other factors that can influence decisions about science, and the way science is used:

Economic issues: Society can't always afford to do things scientists recommend without cutting back elsewhere (e.g. investing heavily in alternative energy sources).

Social issues: Decisions based on scientific evidence affect people — e.g. should fossil fuels be taxed more highly (to invest in alternative energy)? Should alcohol be banned (to prevent health problems)? Would the effect on people's lifestyles be acceptable...

Environmental issues: Nuclear power stations can provide us with a reliable source of electricity, but disposing of the waste can lead to environmental issues.

Ethical issues: There are a lot of things that scientific developments have made possible, but should we do them? E.g. develop better nuclear weapons.

Not revising — a definite drawback in the exam...

Developments in science involve a lot of weighing up — new technologies have risks, but the benefits are often huge. Then there are the economic, social, environmental and ethical issues to think about...

Science Has Limits

Science can give us amazing things — cures for diseases, space travel, heated toilet seats...
But science has its limitations — there are questions that it just can't answer.

Some Questions Are Unanswered by Science — So Far

1) We don't understand everything. And we never will. We'll find out more, for sure — as more hypotheses are suggested, and more experiments are done. But there'll always be stuff we don't know.

> EXAMPLES:
> - Today we don't know as much as we'd like about the impacts of global warming. How much will sea level rise? And to what extent will weather patterns change?
> - We also don't know anywhere near as much as we'd like about the universe. Are there other life forms out there? And what is the universe made of?

2) These are complicated questions. At the moment, scientists don't all agree on the answers because there isn't enough evidence.

3) But eventually, we probably will be able to answer these questions once and for all...
...all we need is more evidence.

4) But by then there'll be loads of new questions to answer.

Other Questions Are Unanswerable by Science

1) Then there's the other type... questions that all the experiments in the world won't help us answer — the "Should we be doing this at all?" type questions. There are always two sides...

2) Take space exploration. It's possible to do it — but does that mean we should?

3) Different people have different opinions.

> For example...
> Some people say it's a good idea... it increases our knowledge about the Universe, we develop new technologies that can be useful on Earth too, it inspires young people to take an interest in science, etc.
> Other people say it's a bad idea... the vast sums of money it costs should be spent on more urgent problems, like providing clean drinking water and curing diseases in poor countries. Others say that we should concentrate research efforts on understanding our own planet better first.

4) This question of whether something is morally or ethically right or wrong can't be answered by more experiments — there is no "right" or "wrong" answer.

5) The best we can do is get a consensus from society — a judgement that most people are more or less happy to live by. Science can provide more information to help people make this judgement, and the judgement might change over time. But in the end it's up to people and their conscience.

Chips or rice? — totally unanswerable by science...

Right — get this straight in your head — science can't tell you whether you should or shouldn't do something. That kind of thing is up to you and society to decide. There are tons of questions that science might be able to answer in the future — like how much sea level might rise due to global warming, what the Universe is made of and whatever happened to those pink stripy socks with Santa on that I used to have.

Planning Experiments

That's all the dull stuff about the world of science over — now to the hands-on part. The next few pages show how <u>experiments</u> should be carried out — by both <u>professional scientists</u> and <u>you</u>.

An Experiment Must be a Fair Test

1) One of the most important parts of planning an experiment is making sure that the <u>evidence</u> you collect is <u>valid</u> and <u>reliable</u> (see page 2). This means that your experiment must be a <u>fair test</u>.

2) The only way to make it a fair test is to <u>change</u> only <u>one variable</u> (factor) in the experiment. All the <u>other variables</u> should <u>be controlled</u> — they should <u>stay exactly the same</u> throughout the experiment and each time the experiment is repeated.

3) For example, say you're looking at the effect of the <u>angle of a slope</u> on the time taken for a toy car to travel down it. You need to keep the <u>slope length</u> the same — otherwise you won't know if any change in the time taken is caused by the change in angle or the change in length.

The Equipment Used Has to be Right for the Job

When you're planning an experiment, you need to make sure you choose the <u>right equipment</u>. For example, the measuring equipment you use has to be <u>sensitive enough</u> to accurately measure the chemicals you're using, e.g. if you need to measure out 11 ml of a liquid, you'll need to use a measuring cylinder that can measure to 1 ml, not 5 or 10 ml.

An Experiment Must be Safe

1) Part of planning an experiment is making sure that it's <u>safe</u>.

2) There are lots of <u>hazards</u> you could be faced with during an experiment, e.g. <u>radiation</u>, <u>electricity</u>, <u>gas</u> and <u>fire</u>.

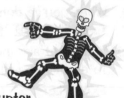

3) You should always make sure that you <u>identify</u> all the hazards that you might encounter.

4) You should also come up with ways of <u>reducing the risks</u> from the hazards you've identified.

5) One way of doing this is to carry out a <u>risk assessment</u>:

> For an experiment involving a <u>Bunsen burner</u>, the risk assessment might be something like this:

> <u>Hazard:</u> Bunsen burner is a fire risk.
>
> <u>Precautions:</u>
> * Keep flammable chemicals away from the Bunsen.
> * Never leave the Bunsen unattended when lit.
> * Always turn on the yellow safety flame when not in use.

Repeats affect Reliability, and Range of Measurements affects Validity

1) One way to make data <u>more reliable</u> is to <u>repeat</u> the measurements and take an <u>average</u> (see next page).

2) Also, the <u>range of data</u> collected has to be <u>suitable</u>, and you need to take <u>enough measurements</u> throughout the <u>whole</u> of the range — otherwise you won't be able to identify the <u>pattern</u> you're looking for. For example, if your hypothesis is that the angle of a slope affects the time taken for a toy car to travel down it, you'd need to measure the time at a wide range of angles, e.g. 20° to 80°, and in 5° steps throughout the range.

3) If the range isn't big enough, or you don't take enough measurements throughout the range, your data <u>won't</u> be <u>valid</u> for the <u>hypothesis</u> you're supposed to be testing.

> Take a look back at page 2 if you can't remember what reliability and validity are.

Reliable data — it won't ever forget your birthday...

All this stuff is really important — without <u>good quality</u> data an investigation will be totally <u>meaningless</u>. So give this page a read through a couple of times and your data will be the envy of the whole scientific community.

Collecting, Processing and Presenting Data

After you've collected your data you'll have <u>oodles of info</u> that you have to <u>make some kind of sense of</u>. You need to <u>process</u> and <u>present</u> it so you can look for <u>patterns</u> and <u>relationships</u> in it.

Data Needs to be Organised

1) <u>Tables</u> are dead useful for <u>recording results</u> and <u>organising data</u>.

2) When you draw a table, make sure that <u>each column</u> has a <u>heading</u> and that you've included the <u>units</u>.

3) Annoyingly, tables are about as useful as a chocolate teapot for showing <u>patterns</u> or <u>relationships</u> in data. You need to use some kind of graph for that (see below).

Check For Mistakes Made When Collecting Data

1) When you've collected all the results for an experiment, you should have a look to see if there are any results that <u>don't seem to fit</u> in with the rest.

2) Most results vary a bit, but any that are totally different are called <u>anomalous results</u>.

3) If you ever get any anomalous results, you should investigate them to try to <u>work out what happened</u>. If you can work out what happened (e.g. you measured something wrong) you can <u>ignore</u> them when processing and presenting your data.

Data Can be Processed Using a Bit of Maths

1) When you've done repeats of an experiment you should always calculate the <u>mean</u> (average). To do this <u>ADD TOGETHER</u> all the data values and <u>DIVIDE</u> by the total number of values in the sample.

2) You might also need to calculate the <u>range</u> (how spread out the data is). To do this find the <u>LARGEST</u> number and <u>SUBTRACT</u> the <u>SMALLEST</u> number from it. *Ignore anomalous results when calculating these.*

EXAMPLE:

Test tube	Repeat 1 (g)	Repeat 2 (g)	Repeat 3 (g)	Mean (g)	Range (g)
A	28	37	32	(28 + 37 + 32) ÷ 3 = 32.3	37 − 28 = 9
B	47	51	60	(47 + 51 + 60) ÷ 3 = 52.7	60 − 47 = 13
C	68	72	70	(68 + 72 + 70) ÷ 3 = 70.0	72 − 68 = 4

If Your Data Comes in Categories, Present It in a Bar Chart

1) If one of the variables is <u>categoric</u> (comes in distinct categories, e.g. blood types, metals) you should use a <u>bar chart</u> to display the data.

2) You can also use a bar chart if one of the variables is <u>discrete</u> (the data can only take whole values and there are no in-between ones, e.g. number of people is discrete because you can't have half a person).

3) There are some <u>golden rules</u> you need to follow for <u>drawing</u> bar charts:

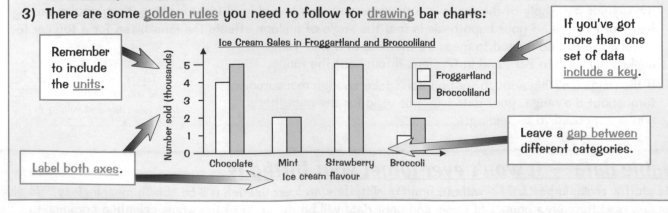

Remember to include the <u>units</u>.

If you've got more than one set of data <u>include a key</u>.

Label both axes.

Leave a <u>gap between</u> different categories.

Ice Cream Sales in Froggartland and Broccoliland

Number sold (thousands)

Chocolate   Mint   Strawberry   Broccoli
Ice cream flavour

Froggartland
Broccoliland

Collecting, Processing and Presenting Data

If Your Data is Continuous, Plot a Line Graph

1) If both the variables are continuous (numerical data that can have any value within a range, e.g. length, volume, temperature) you should use a line graph to display the data.

2) Here are the rules for drawing line graphs:

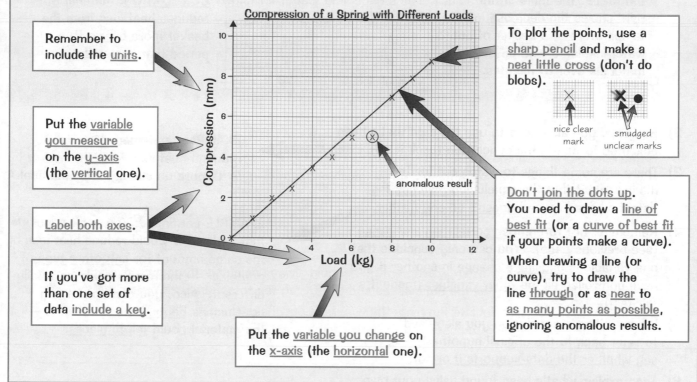

Remember to include the units.

Put the variable you measure on the y-axis (the vertical one).

Label both axes.

If you've got more than one set of data include a key.

Put the variable you change on the x-axis (the horizontal one).

To plot the points, use a sharp pencil and make a neat little cross (don't do blobs).

nice clear mark | smudged unclear marks

anomalous result

Don't join the dots up. You need to draw a line of best fit (or a curve of best fit if your points make a curve).

When drawing a line (or curve), try to draw the line through or as near to as many points as possible, ignoring anomalous results.

Line Graphs Can Show Relationships in Data

1) Line graphs are used to show the relationship between two variables (just like other graphs).

2) Data can show three different types of correlation (relationship):

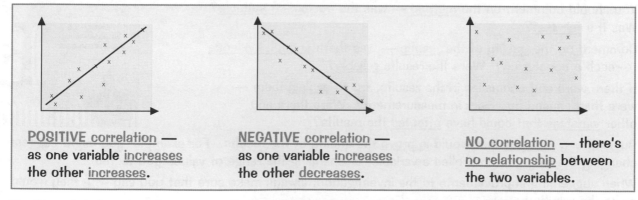

POSITIVE correlation — as one variable increases the other increases.

NEGATIVE correlation — as one variable increases the other decreases.

NO correlation — there's no relationship between the two variables.

3) You've got to be careful not to confuse correlation with cause though. A correlation just means that there's a relationship between two variables. It doesn't mean that the change in one variable is causing the change in the other (there might be other factors involved).

There's a positive correlation between age of man and length of nose hair...

Collect, process, present... data's like a difficult child — it needs a lot of attention. Go on, make it happy.

Drawing Conclusions and Evaluating

At the end of an experiment, the <u>conclusion</u> and <u>evaluation</u> are waiting. Don't worry, they won't bite.

You Can Only Conclude What the Data Shows and NO MORE

1) Drawing a conclusion can be quite straightforward — just <u>look at your data</u> and <u>say what pattern you see</u> between the variables.

EXAMPLE: The table on the right shows the decrease in temperature of a beaker of hot water insulated with different materials over 10 minutes.

Material	Mean temperature decrease (°C)
A	4
B	2
No Insulation	20

CONCLUSION: Material <u>B</u> reduces heat loss from the beaker more over a <u>10 minute</u> period than material A.

2) However, you also need to use the data that's been <u>collected</u> to <u>justify</u> the conclusion (back it up).

EXAMPLE continued: Material B reduced heat loss from the beaker by 2 °C more on average than material A.

3) There are some things to watch out for too — it's important that the conclusion <u>matches the data</u> it's based on and <u>doesn't go any further</u>.

4) Remember not to <u>confuse correlation</u> and <u>cause</u> (see previous page). You can only conclude that one variable is <u>causing</u> a change in another if you have controlled <u>all</u> the <u>other variables</u> (made it a <u>fair test</u>).

EXAMPLE continued: You can't conclude that material B would reduce heat loss by the same amount for <u>any other type of container</u> — the results could be totally different. Also, you can't make any conclusions <u>beyond</u> the 10 minutes — the material could <u>fall to pieces</u>.

5) When writing a conclusion you also need to <u>refer back</u> to the original hypothesis — say whether the data <u>supports it</u> or not.

6) Then <u>explain</u> what's been found using your own <u>scientific knowledge</u> (what you've learnt in class).

Evaluation — Describe How You Could Improve the Investigation

1) You should comment on the <u>method</u> — was the <u>equipment suitable</u>? Was it a <u>fair test</u>?

2) Comment on the <u>quality</u> of the <u>results</u> — was there <u>enough evidence</u> to reach a <u>conclusion</u>? Were the results <u>reliable</u>?

3) If there were any anomalies in the results, try to <u>explain</u> them — were they caused by <u>errors</u> in measurement? Were there any other <u>variables</u> that could have <u>affected</u> the results?

I'd value this E somewhere in the region of 250-300k

4) Suggest any <u>changes</u> that would <u>improve</u> the quality of the results. For example, you might suggest changing the way you controlled a variable, or changing the range of values you tested.

5) When suggesting improvements to the investigation, always make sure that you say <u>why</u> they would make the results <u>better</u>.

Evaluation — next time, I will make sure I don't burn the lab down...

I know it doesn't seem very nice, but writing about where you went <u>wrong</u> is an important skill — it shows you'v got a really good understanding of what the investigation was <u>about</u>. It's difficult for me — I'm always right.

The Controlled Assessment

You'll probably carry out a few investigations as you go through the course, but at some point you'll have to do the one that counts... the <u>controlled assessment</u>. Here's a bit about it...

The Controlled Assessment is Split into Three Parts

Part A — Planning

For this part you'll be given some information about a topic. Then you'll have to develop a <u>hypothesis</u> and <u>plan an experiment</u> to <u>test it</u>. Write a <u>method</u> in a logical <u>step-by-step</u> order — you'll need to decide:

1) What <u>variables</u> you're going to <u>control</u> — and <u>how</u> you're going to control them.
2) What <u>equipment</u> to use — and say <u>why</u> you've chosen each bit of kit.
3) What <u>risks</u> are involved in the experiment — and say <u>how</u> you're going to <u>reduce</u> each of them.
4) The <u>range of measurements</u> you're going to take — and say <u>why</u> you've chosen that range.
5) How many times you'll <u>repeat</u> each measurement. You should do <u>at least two</u> repeats to make your data <u>more reliable</u>.

There's lots of help on all of these things on page 5.

You'll also need to say why your method is <u>suitable</u> for testing the hypothesis.

Part B — Observations

For Part B you'll be testing the hypothesis you developed in Part A by <u>carrying out the experiment</u> you planned. You'll need to:

1) Take an appropriate <u>number</u> and <u>range</u> of measurements (see page 5).
2) <u>Repeat</u> your measurements to get more <u>reliable data</u> (if possible) — <u>two times</u> is a good idea.
3) <u>Record</u> your data clearly in a nice, neat <u>table</u> (see page 6 for table tips).

Also, you'll need to find some <u>secondary data</u> (data collected by other people) that's relevant to the hypothesis. Make sure you say <u>where</u> you got the data from, and say <u>how good quality</u> the source was.

Part C — Conclusions

This part involves <u>processing</u> data, <u>presenting</u> data, drawing <u>conclusions</u> and <u>evaluating</u>. You'll have to do these things for your data (<u>primary data</u>), but also for the <u>secondary data</u> you collected in Part B. You'll need to:

1) <u>Process all the data</u> (both primary and secondary), e.g. calculate the mean (see page 6).
2) <u>Present all the data</u> using the right type of <u>graph</u> for each (see pages 6-7 for help with this).
3) Identify any <u>anomalous results</u> and explain why you didn't include them when you processed and presented your data (they'd reduce the validity of your results). If there <u>aren't</u> any anomalous results, then you need to <u>say so</u>.
4) Write <u>conclusions</u> that cover all the data (see previous page for what to say). Make sure you <u>back up</u> your conclusions using the data, say <u>whether the conclusions support the hypothesis</u> or not and <u>explain what's been found</u> using your own knowledge.
5) Write an <u>evaluation</u> (see previous page for what to include). Don't forget to say <u>how</u> the method affected the results, and how any improvements would make the results better.
6) Use your evaluation to say how <u>confident</u> you are in your conclusions. Think about <u>other evidence</u> that you could collect to give <u>stronger support</u> for your conclusions.

Keep your assessment under control — read this page...

Pretty straightforward, eh? As long as you've <u>learnt everything</u> on the previous few pages, you should be fine. Make sure you <u>know</u> each section like the <u>back of your hand</u> before you come to do the assessment itself.

Changing Ideas About the Solar System

Our Solar System is made up of a <u>star</u> (<u>the Sun</u>) and lots of stuff <u>orbiting</u> it in <u>slightly elongated</u> circles (called ellipses). But <u>scientists</u> and <u>astronomers</u> didn't always think the Universe and our Solar System was like that...

Ancient Greeks Thought the Earth was the Centre of the Universe

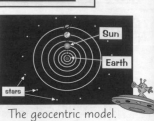

The geocentric model.

1) Most ancient Greek astronomers believed that the Sun, Moon, planets and stars all <u>orbited the Earth</u> in perfect <u>circles</u> — this is known as the <u>geocentric model</u>.

2) The <u>geocentric model</u> was the accepted model of the Universe from the time of the <u>ancient Greeks</u> until the 1500s. It was only in the 1600s that it began to be replaced by the <u>heliocentric model</u>.

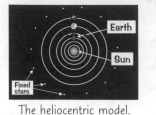

The heliocentric model.

3) The <u>heliocentric model</u> states that the Earth and planets all <u>orbit the Sun</u>, which is at the <u>centre</u> of the Universe.

4) The heliocentric idea had already been around for 2000 years, but the <u>model</u> was first introduced in a book by <u>Copernicus</u> in 1543. This book showed astronomical observations could be explained <u>without</u> having the <u>Earth</u> at the centre of the Universe.

5) Copernicus' ideas <u>weren't</u> popular at the time, and the model itself was condemned by the <u>Church</u>. One of the most convincing pieces of evidence for this theory was <u>Galileo's observations</u> of Jupiter's moons.

> In 1610, Galileo was observing Jupiter using a <u>telescope</u> (a <u>new invention</u> at the time) when he saw <u>three stars</u> in a line near the planet. When he looked again the next evening, he saw these stars had moved in the <u>wrong</u> direction in the night sky. After a week, a <u>fourth</u> star appeared. These stars <u>never</u> moved away from Jupiter and seemed to be <u>carried along</u> with the planet — he realised these four objects weren't stars, but <u>moons orbiting Jupiter</u>. This showed <u>not everything</u> was in orbit around the Earth — which proved the geocentric model was <u>wrong</u>.

6) The current model still says that the planets in our Solar System <u>orbit</u> the Sun — but that these orbits are actually <u>elliptical</u> rather than circular.

7) As <u>technology</u> has improved, our idea of the <u>Solar System</u> and the Universe has changed. E.g. the invention of the <u>telescope</u> led to the discovery of <u>Uranus</u>.

Our current view of the Solar System.

Visible Light Can Tell Us a Lot About the Universe

1) Most of the stuff <u>scientists</u> know about the <u>Universe</u> comes from <u>detecting waves</u> from objects in space. Some objects like stars are <u>huge</u>, very <u>hot</u> and very <u>far away</u> from us. They <u>give out</u> lots of <u>visible light</u> — which is why you can see them, even though they're very far away. We can see the <u>planets</u> in our Solar System because they <u>reflect</u> sunlight.

2) Early astronomers made observations of the Universe just using the <u>naked eye</u>. Many very <u>important</u> <u>discoveries</u> of <u>stars</u>, <u>comets</u> and <u>planets</u> were made this way. Most astronomical objects are so <u>far away</u> and look so small that naked eye observations are only really useful for <u>mapping</u> their positions.

3) <u>Telescopes</u> magnify images, so distant objects can be seen in <u>more detail</u>. You can also see objects that are at <u>larger</u> distances. Many new objects have been discovered using telescopes and they've helped us <u>learn more</u> about the what the Universe is <u>made up</u> of (p.24). Telescopes on Earth have problems though (p.23). <u>Space telescopes</u> overcome these issues — but they're <u>expensive</u>.

4) <u>Photographs</u> of the Universe can be taken using <u>telescopes</u> — this allows you to '<u>zoom in</u>' and look at objects in <u>more detail</u>. It makes it easier to <u>monitor</u> an object by taking pictures at different <u>times</u> to compare them, and to <u>share</u> your observations with others. You can also see faint objects by allowing a <u>long exposure time</u> so you collect more light — which obviously <u>can't</u> be done with just the naked eye.

Make a model, prove it wrong, make a model, prove it wrong...

It's taken <u>thousands</u> of years for us to reach our <u>current model</u> of the Solar System. Although the geocentric and heliocentric models turned out to be wrong, they played a <u>really important part</u> in helping us reach the model we have today. And unsurprisingly, there's <u>loads</u> that scientists <u>still</u> don't know about our Solar System...

Waves — Basic Principles

Visible light, infrared, ultrasound and so on — they're all <u>waves</u>, and they have certain features in common.

All Waves Have Wavelength, Frequency, Amplitude and Speed

1) <u>WAVELENGTH</u> is the distance from one peak to the next.
2) <u>FREQUENCY</u> is how many <u>complete waves</u> there are <u>per second</u> (passing a certain point). It's measured in <u>hertz</u> (Hz). 1 <u>Hz</u> is 1 wave per second. High frequencies are often given in <u>kHz</u> (1 kHz = 1000 Hz) or <u>MHz</u> (1 MHz = 1 000 000 Hz).
3) <u>AMPLITUDE</u> is just the height of the wave (from the mid-line to the peak).
4) The <u>SPEED</u> is, well, how fast it goes.
5) One <u>important</u> thing to remember is that <u>waves transfer energy and information</u> — <u>without</u> transferring <u>matter</u>.

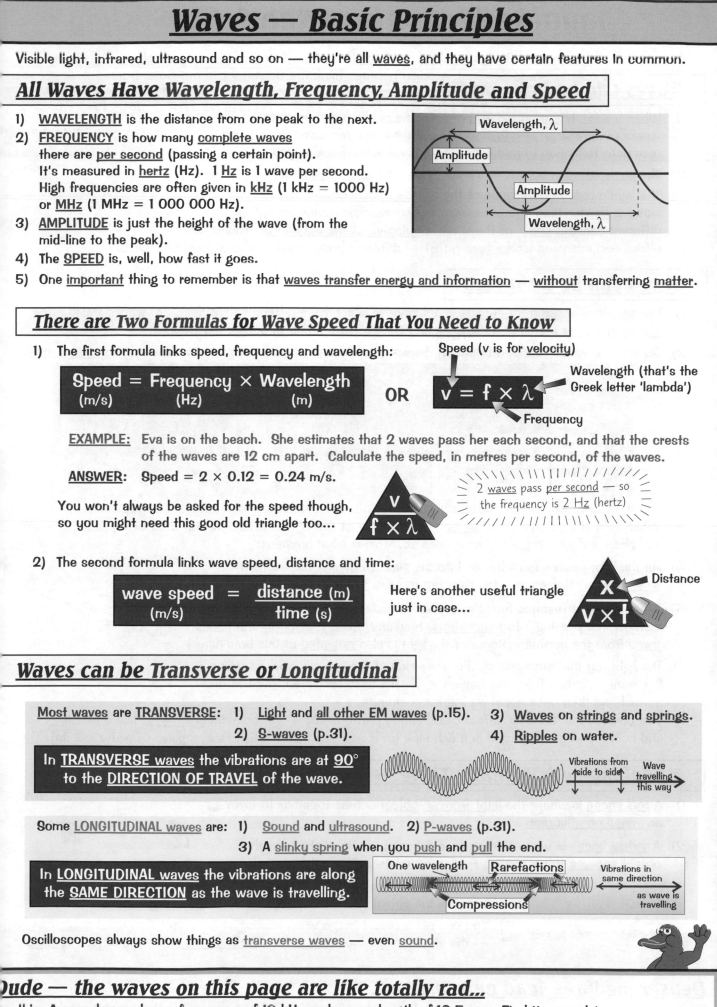

There are Two Formulas for Wave Speed That You Need to Know

1) The first formula links speed, frequency and wavelength:

$$\text{Speed} = \text{Frequency} \times \text{Wavelength}$$
(m/s)   (Hz)   (m)

Speed (v is for <u>velocity</u>)

OR $$v = f \times \lambda$$

Wavelength (that's the Greek letter 'lambda')

Frequency

EXAMPLE: Eva is on the beach. She estimates that 2 waves pass her each second, and that the crests of the waves are 12 cm apart. Calculate the speed, in metres per second, of the waves.

ANSWER: Speed = 2 × 0.12 = 0.24 m/s.

You won't always be asked for the speed though, so you might need this good old triangle too...

$$\frac{v}{f \times \lambda}$$

2 <u>waves</u> pass <u>per second</u> — so the frequency is <u>2 Hz</u> (hertz)

2) The second formula links wave speed, distance and time:

$$\text{wave speed} = \frac{\text{distance (m)}}{\text{time (s)}}$$
(m/s)

Here's another useful triangle just in case...

$$\frac{x}{v \times t}$$

Distance

Waves can be Transverse or Longitudinal

<u>Most waves</u> are <u>TRANSVERSE</u>:
1) <u>Light</u> and <u>all other EM waves</u> (p.15).
2) <u>S-waves</u> (p.31).
3) <u>Waves</u> on <u>strings</u> and <u>springs</u>.
4) <u>Ripples</u> on water.

In <u>TRANSVERSE</u> waves the vibrations are at <u>90°</u> to the <u>DIRECTION OF TRAVEL</u> of the wave.

Vibrations from side to side

Wave travelling this way

Some <u>LONGITUDINAL</u> waves are:
1) <u>Sound</u> and <u>ultrasound</u>.
2) <u>P-waves</u> (p.31).
3) A <u>slinky spring</u> when you <u>push</u> and <u>pull</u> the end.

In <u>LONGITUDINAL</u> waves the vibrations are along the <u>SAME DIRECTION</u> as the wave is travelling.

One wavelength   Rarefactions

Compressions

Vibrations in same direction as wave is travelling

Oscilloscopes always show things as <u>transverse waves</u> — even <u>sound</u>.

Dude — the waves on this page are like totally rad...

Try this: A sound wave has a frequency of 19 kHz and a wavelength of 12.5 cm. Find its speed.*

Reflection and Refraction

All waves can be <u>reflected</u>. They can also be <u>refracted</u> — it's a fancy way of saying '<u>change direction</u>'.

Waves Can be Reflected

1) When a wave hits a boundary between one medium and another, some of its energy is <u>reflected</u>. This is why you can sometimes see your reflection in puddles — light is reflected back at you.

2) The <u>angle of reflection</u>, r, is the same as the <u>angle of incidence</u>, i.

3) The light's reflected because of the <u>change in density</u> — water is <u>denser</u> than <u>air</u>. Whenever a wave reaches a medium with a different density, <u>some</u> of the wave is <u>reflected at the boundary</u>. This is how ultrasound scanning works (see p.28) — different body tissues have different densities.

Reflected ray   r   i   Incident ray

the line at right angles to the surface is called the <u>normal</u>.

Puddle

Waves Can be Refracted

1) Waves travel at <u>different speeds</u> in substances which have <u>different densities</u>. EM waves travel more <u>slowly</u> in <u>denser</u> media (usually). Sound waves travel faster in <u>denser</u> substances.

2) So when a wave crosses a boundary between two substances, from glass to air, say, it <u>changes speed</u>.

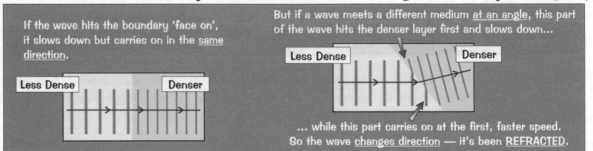

If the wave hits the boundary 'face on', it slows down but carries on in the <u>same direction</u>.

Less Dense   Denser

But if a wave meets a different medium <u>at an angle</u>, this part of the wave hits the denser layer first and slows down...

Less Dense   Denser

... while this part carries on at the first, faster speed. So the wave <u>changes direction</u> — it's been <u>REFRACTED</u>.

3) When light shines on a glass <u>window pane</u>, some of the light is reflected, but a lot of it passes through the glass and gets <u>refracted</u> as it does so. This is what happens:

4) As the light passes from the air into the glass (a <u>denser</u> medium), it <u>slows down</u>. This causes the light ray to bend <u>towards</u> the normal.

5) When the light reaches the 'glass to air' boundary on the other side of the window, it's passing into a <u>less dense</u> medium. So it <u>speeds up</u> and bends <u>away</u> from the normal. (Some of the light is also <u>reflected</u> at this boundary.)

6) The light ray that emerges on the other side of the glass is now travelling in the same direction it was to begin with — it's been refracted towards the normal and then back again by the same amount.

Emerge ray
window glass
Refracted ray
i
Incident ray

7) You can see the 'bending' effect of refraction pretty easily — get something <u>straight</u>, like a pencil, and hold it partly submerged in a fish tank (or if you don't have a fish tank, a glass of water will do).

A Real Image is Actually There — A Virtual Image Is Not

1) A <u>real image</u> is where the <u>light from an object</u> comes together to form an <u>image on a 'screen'</u>.

2) A <u>virtual image</u> is when the rays are diverging, so the light from the object <u>appears</u> to be coming from a completely <u>different place</u>.

lens   REAL IMAGE on screen
OBJECT

VIRTUAL IMAGE   lens   OBJECT

3) When you look in a <u>mirror</u> you see a <u>virtual image</u> of your face — because the <u>object</u> (your face) <u>appears</u> to be <u>behind the mirror</u>.

4) You can get a virtual image when looking at an object through a <u>magnifying lens</u> — the virtual image looks <u>bigger</u> and <u>further away</u> than the object <u>actually</u> is.

Denser media — lead newspapers...

Learn the straightforward rule: <u>more dense</u> materials <u>slow light down</u>, <u>less dense</u> materials <u>speed it up</u>.

Lenses

Lenses are usually made of glass or plastic. All lenses change the <u>direction of light rays</u> by <u>refraction</u>.

Converging Lenses are Used to Focus Light

1) A <u>converging</u> lens is <u>convex</u> — it <u>bulges outwards</u>. It causes parallel rays of <u>light</u> to converge (move <u>together</u>) to a <u>focus</u>.

2) The <u>axis</u> of a lens is a line passing through the <u>middle</u> of the lens.

3) The <u>focal point</u> is where rays hitting the lens parallel to the axis all <u>meet</u>.

4) Each lens has a focal point <u>in front</u> of the lens, and one <u>behind</u>.

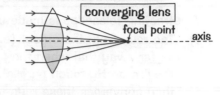

Draw a Ray Diagram for an Image Through a Converging Lens

1) Pick a point on the <u>top</u> of the object. Draw a ray going from the object to the lens <u>parallel</u> to the axis of the lens.

2) Draw another ray from the top of the object going right through the middle of the lens.

3) The incident ray that's <u>parallel</u> to the axis is <u>refracted</u> through the <u>focal point</u>. Draw a <u>refracted ray</u> passing through the <u>focal point</u>.

4) The ray passing through the <u>middle</u> of the lens doesn't bend.

5) Mark where the rays <u>meet</u>. That's the <u>top of the image</u>.

6) Repeat the process for a point on the bottom of the object. When the bottom of the object is on the <u>axis</u>, the bottom of the image is <u>also</u> on the axis.

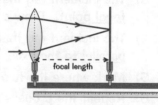

Focal Length is the Distance From the Lens to its Focal Point

A simple <u>experiment</u> can be used to work out the <u>focal length</u> of a converging lens:

1) Clamp the lens at one end of a <u>track</u>. Then clamp a piece of white card <u>further</u> down the track.

2) Set up this equipment near a window with the lens directed at a <u>distant object</u>, e.g. a nearby building — you should be able to see an <u>image</u> of the object on the piece of card. Turn off any lights in the room to make the image more visible.

3) Move the card along the track until the image is <u>focused</u> (this is where the picture looks <u>sharpest</u>). When you've got the best image you can — clamp the piece of card in place so it doesn't move.

4) Use a <u>ruler</u> to measure the <u>distance</u> between the <u>centre</u> of the lens and the card — this is the <u>focal length</u>.

Distance from the Lens Affects the Image

You can also do an <u>experiment</u> to find out <u>how</u> an object's distance from the lens affects the image:

1) Use the same apparatus as above — this time put an <u>object</u> on the <u>other</u> side of the lens to the card.

2) Move the object <u>away</u> from the lens and move the card until you get a <u>focused</u> image of the object. The object should be <u>well lit</u>, but the screen shouldn't (to make the image easier to see). Make a note of the <u>distance</u> from the object to the lens, and from the lens to the card. Do this a few times with the object at <u>different</u> distances from the lens. You should find:

a) An object <u>at 2F</u> will produce a <u>real</u>, <u>upside down</u> image the <u>same size</u> as the object, and <u>at 2F</u>.

b) <u>Between F and 2F</u> it'll make a <u>real</u>, <u>upside down</u> image <u>bigger</u> than the object, and <u>beyond 2F</u>.

c) An object <u>nearer than F</u> won't appear on the screen, but will make a <u>virtual</u> image the <u>right way up</u>, <u>bigger</u> than the object, on the <u>same side</u> of the lens.

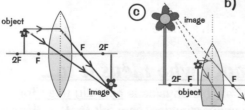
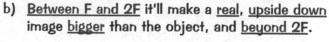

Simple and Reflecting Telescopes

Converging lenses are used in optical telescopes — these are telescopes that collect and focus light.
The two types you need to know about are simple refracting telescopes and reflecting telescopes.

A Refracting Telescope uses Two Converging Lenses

A refracting telescope is made up of an objective lens and an eyepiece lens.

1) The rays from the object (e.g. a star) are coming from
so far away that when they reach the objective lens
they're pretty much parallel. The objective lens
then converges these rays to form a real image
at the focal point of the objective lens.

2) The rays of light from the real image enter the eyepiece lens.
The lens spreads them out so they leave at a wider angle than they
entered it — and so the light rays fill more of your retina (the 'screen'
at the back of your eye) — this makes the image look magnified (bigger).

You don't need to
know how to draw this
diagram — hoorah.

parallel rays
from object
in space

objective lens

real
image

magnified virtual
image at infinity

eyepiece le

Concave Mirrors are Shiny on the Inside of the Curve

To understand how a reflecting telescope works you first need to know how a concave mirror works —
and how a ray diagram of a reflection in one is drawn...

> 1) An incident ray parallel to the axis will pass through the focal point when it's reflected.
>
> 2) An incident ray passing through the focal point will be parallel to the axis when it's reflected.

1) Pick a point on the top of the object. Draw a ray going from the
object to the mirror parallel to the axis of the mirror.

2) Draw another line going from the top of the object to the mirror,
passing through the focal point on the way.

3) The incident ray that's parallel to the axis is reflected through the
focal point. Draw a reflected ray passing through the focal point.

4) The incident ray that passes through the focal point is reflected
parallel to the axis. Draw a reflected ray passing parallel to the axis.

5) Mark where the two reflected rays meet. That's the top of the image.

6) Repeat the process for a point on the bottom of the object. When the
bottom of the object is on the axis, the bottom of the image is also on the axis.

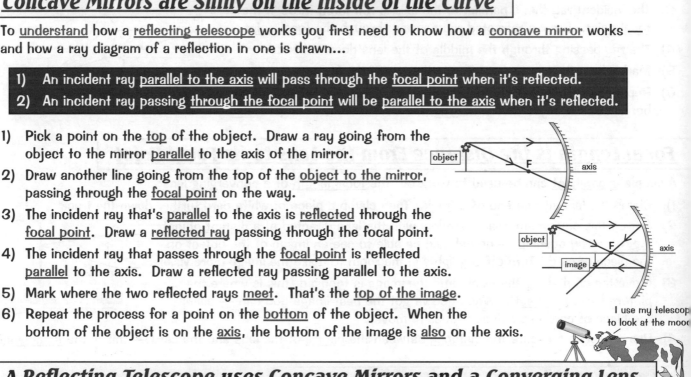

object   F   axis

object   F   axis
image

I use my telescop
to look at the moo

A Reflecting Telescope uses Concave Mirrors and a Converging Lens

Many reflecting telescopes look like this:

1) A large concave mirror collects the parallel
rays of light from an object in space.

2) The larger mirror reflects this light onto a
smaller second mirror placed in front of
the large mirror's focal point.

3) The smaller mirror reflects the light through a
hole in the centre of the large collecting mirror.
A real image is formed behind the mirror.

4) A converging eyepiece lens is used to magnify this image — just like in the refracting telescope.

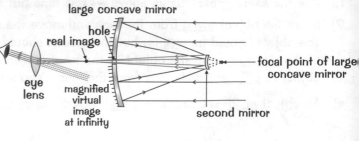

large concave mirror

hole
real image

eye
lens

magnified
virtual
image
at infinity

focal point of large
concave mirror

second mirror

I can't find my telescope — I wonder who I lens it to...

They're quite keen on making sure you know what all this physics is actually used for. In this case, it's the joys
of telescopes. Make sure you're happy with how converging lenses work first — then get to grips with this page.

Electromagnetic Waves

You almost certainly use electromagnetic waves every day of your life — so learn to love them.

There are Seven Types of Electromagnetic (EM) Waves

The EM spectrum is split into seven groups — these are shown below with their wavelengths.
The groups shown actually merge into each other — forming a continuous spectrum.

	RADIO WAVES	MICRO WAVES	INFRA RED	VISIBLE LIGHT	ULTRA VIOLET	X-RAYS	GAMMA RAYS
wavelength	$1\,m - 10^4\,m$	$10^{-2}\,m$ (1 cm)	$10^{-5}\,m$ (0.01 mm)	$10^{-7}\,m$	$10^{-8}\,m$	$10^{-10}\,m$	$10^{-12}\,m$

INCREASING FREQUENCY AND DECREASING WAVELENGTH →

1) All EM waves are transverse waves (see page 11).

2) All the different types of EM wave travel at the same speed (3×10^8 m/s) in a vacuum, e.g. in space.

3) This means EM waves with higher frequencies, like X-rays and γ-rays (gamma rays), have shorter wavelengths.

Infrared Radiation was Discovered by Herschel in 1800

Up until the discovery of infrared radiation (see page 18), visible light was the only part of the EM spectrum that scientists knew existed. Herschel found infrared when experimenting with sunlight and a prism:

1) When white light goes through a prism, it creates a spectrum of colours (see diagram below). Herschel used this equipment to create a spectrum on a screen.

2) He wanted to know about the amount of heat in each of these colours — he used a thermometer to measure each colour's temperature in turn. He noticed they increased from violet to red.

3) He then measured the temperature just past the red part of the spectrum where there was no visible light. He found here had the highest temperature of all — he had discovered infrared, an invisible type of radiation.

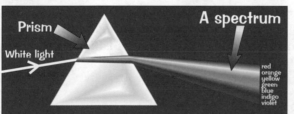

Prism
White light
A spectrum
red
orange
yellow
green
blue
indigo
violet

You might be asked how to carry out Herschel and Ritter's experiments in the exam — so make sure you learn them.

Ritter Discovered Ultraviolet Radiation Soon After in 1801

A scientist called Ritter began to carry out experiments to see if he could find anything on the other side of the spectrum beyond violet.

1) Ritter knew silver chloride turned from white to black when exposed to light. So he decided to measure how quickly silver chloride coated strips changed when exposed to different colours of light.

2) In a dark room, he created a spectrum using a light source and a prism and exposed the strips of paper to each colour. He timed how long it took the strips to turn black.

3) The strips changed quickest when exposed to light nearer the blue end of the spectrum.

4) He then placed a strip in the area just past the violet part of the spectrum — here he saw the quickest change of all. Ritter had discovered ultraviolet radiation, an invisible form of light that exists on the other side of the visible spectrum.

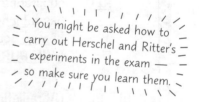

Daily Maily
EXCLUSIVE:
Silver Chloride
Exposed

Herschel and Ritter — not to be confused with Hansel and Gretel...

Herschel and Ritter's work was really important to physics — it showed that other types of waves beyond the visible spectrum existed. Over the next 100 years or so the other types of EM waves (shown in the diagram at the top) were also discovered. One massively important thing to remember about EM waves is that they all travel at the same speed in a vacuum (e.g. space) — those pesky examiners might try to catch you out on that.

The Dangers of Electromagnetic Radiation

You can't escape EM radiation — it's very useful in many ways, but it can be <u>dangerous</u> too.

The Properties of EM Waves Depend on Their Frequency

1) As the <u>frequency</u> of EM radiation changes, its <u>interaction with matter</u> changes — i.e. the way a wave is <u>absorbed</u>, <u>reflected</u> or <u>transmitted</u> by any given substance <u>depends entirely</u> on its <u>frequency</u>.

2) As a rule, the EM waves at <u>each end</u> of the spectrum tend to be able to <u>pass through material</u>, whilst those <u>nearer the middle</u> are <u>absorbed</u>.

3) The <u>effects</u> of <u>EM radiation</u> on humans depends on the <u>frequency</u> of the EM waves, since frequency determines the <u>energy of the waves</u>.

4) Generally, the higher the frequency, the <u>more energy</u> the radiation has, and so the <u>more harmful</u> the radiation.

5) Make sure you know how <u>exposure</u> to each <u>type</u> of <u>radiation</u> in the table below <u>affects human tissue</u>.

Some EM Radiation Can be Harmful to People

INCREASING FREQUENCY ↓

<u>MICRO-WAVES</u> — <u>Microwaves</u> have a <u>similar frequency</u> to the <u>vibrations</u> of many <u>molecules</u>, and so increase these vibrations — resulting in <u>heating</u> (as in <u>microwave ovens</u>). Microwaves can HEAT HUMAN BODY CELLS this way. <u>Mobile phones</u> use <u>microwaves</u>, and their increasing use has caused <u>concern</u>, as the handset is often <u>held close</u> to the <u>brain</u>. There have been <u>suggested</u> links with <u>brain tumours</u>, but <u>nothing</u> has been <u>proved</u>.

<u>INFRA-RED</u> — The <u>infrared</u> range of frequencies can make the <u>surface molecules</u> of any substance <u>vibrate</u> — and like microwaves, this has a <u>heating effect</u>. But infrared has a <u>higher frequency</u>, so carries <u>more energy</u> than microwave radiation. If the <u>human body</u> is exposed to <u>too much infrared</u> radiation, it can cause some nasty SKIN BURNS.

<u>ULTRA-VIOLET</u> — UV radiation has got <u>more energy</u> and a <u>higher</u> frequency than infrared radiation. It's '<u>ionising</u>' — it carries <u>enough energy</u> to knock electrons off atoms. <u>SUNBURN</u> happens when surface skin cells have been damaged by absorbing UV rays in sunlight. This can cause <u>cell mutation or destruction</u>, and SKIN CANCER. The <u>UV</u> in <u>sunlight</u> can also cause EYE DAMAGE.

<u>GAMMA/ X-RAYS</u> — <u>Very high-frequency</u> waves, such as <u>gamma rays</u> and <u>X-rays</u>, are also <u>ionising</u>, and carry <u>much more energy</u> than UV rays. This means they can be <u>much more damaging</u> and they can <u>penetrate further</u> into the body. Like all ionising radiation, they can cause CELL MUTATION or <u>destruction</u>, leading to <u>tissue damage</u> or CANCER (see page 20).

When it comes to how harmful an EM wave is — size really does matter...

The various types of EM radiation all have different properties because they all have <u>different frequencies</u>. Remember that the higher the frequency, the <u>more dangerous</u> an EM wave potentially is. It's not all doom and gloom though — even EM waves with high frequencies (e.g. gamma rays) have really important uses.

Radio Waves and Microwaves

You use EM waves for all sorts of stuff — your satellite TV (and your terrestrial TV), your radio, your microwave oven, your pet dog Jimbo... OK maybe not that last bit.

Radio Waves are Used Mainly for Communications

1) Radio waves are used to broadcast TV and radio signals and to transmit satellite signals (in the same way as microwaves — see below).

2) Long-wave radio (wavelengths of 1 – 10 km) can be transmitted from London, say, and received halfway round the world. That's because long wavelengths bend around the curved surface of the Earth. They also get around hills, into tunnels and all sorts.

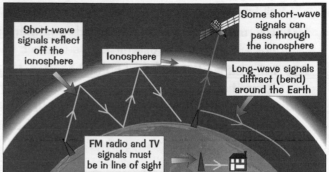

Short-wave signals reflect off the ionosphere

Ionosphere

Some short-wave signals can pass through the ionosphere

Long-wave signals diffract (bend) around the Earth

FM radio and TV signals must be in line of sight

3) The radio waves used for TV and FM radio transmissions have very short wavelengths (10 cm – 10 m). To get reception, you must be in direct sight of the transmitter — the signal doesn't bend around hills or travel far through buildings.

4) Short-wave radio signals (wavelengths of about 10 m – 100 m) can, like long-wave, be received at long distances from the transmitter. That's because they are reflected from the ionosphere — an electrically charged layer in the Earth's upper atmosphere. Medium-wave signals (well, the shorter ones) can also reflect from the ionosphere, depending on atmospheric conditions and time of day.

5) Some very short-wave radio waves can pass through the ionosphere — so they can be used for satellite communications (see below).

Microwaves are Used for Satellite Communication and Mobile Phones

1) Communication to and from satellites (including satellite TV signals and satellite phones) uses microwaves. But you need to use microwaves which can pass easily through the Earth's watery atmosphere.

2) For satellite TV, the signal from a transmitter is transmitted into space...

3) ... where it's picked up by the satellite receiver dish orbiting thousands of kilometres above the Earth. The satellite transmits the signal back to Earth in a different direction...

microwaves

clouds and water vapour

4) ... where it's received by a satellite dish on the ground. There is a slight time delay between the signal being sent and received, e.g. from the UK to Australia, because of the long distance the signal has to travel.

5) Mobile phone signals also travel from your phone to the nearest transmitter as microwaves.

Microwave Ovens Use a Different Microwave Wavelength from Satellites

1) In communications, the microwaves used need to pass through the Earth's watery atmosphere.

2) In microwave ovens, the microwaves need to be absorbed by water molecules in food to be able to heat it up — so they use a different wavelength to those used in satellite communications.

3) The microwaves penetrate up to a few centimetres into the food before being absorbed by water molecules. The energy from the absorbed microwaves causes the food to heat up. The heat energy is then conducted or convected to other parts of the food.

Revision time — adjust depending on brain wattage...

If you're asked for uses of microwaves, then microwave ovens will probably be the first answer you think of. But don't forget they're used in communications too — it's just a different wavelength of microwave that's used.

Infrared Radiation

If you were thinking of turning to a life of crime, beware — waves are out to get you...

Infrared Radiation Can be Used to Monitor Temperature

1) <u>Infrared</u> radiation (or IR) is also known as <u>heat radiation</u>. It's <u>given out</u> by all <u>hot objects</u> — and the <u>hotter</u> the object, the <u>more</u> IR radiation it gives out.

2) This means infrared can be used to <u>monitor temperatures</u>. For example, <u>heat loss</u> through a house's uninsulated roof can be detected using <u>infrared sensors</u>.

3) Infrared is also detected by <u>night-vision equipment</u>. The equipment turns it into an <u>electrical signal</u>, which is <u>displayed on a screen</u> as a picture. The <u>hotter</u> an object is, the <u>brighter</u> it appears. <u>Police</u> and the military use this to spot baddies <u>running away</u>, like you've seen on TV.

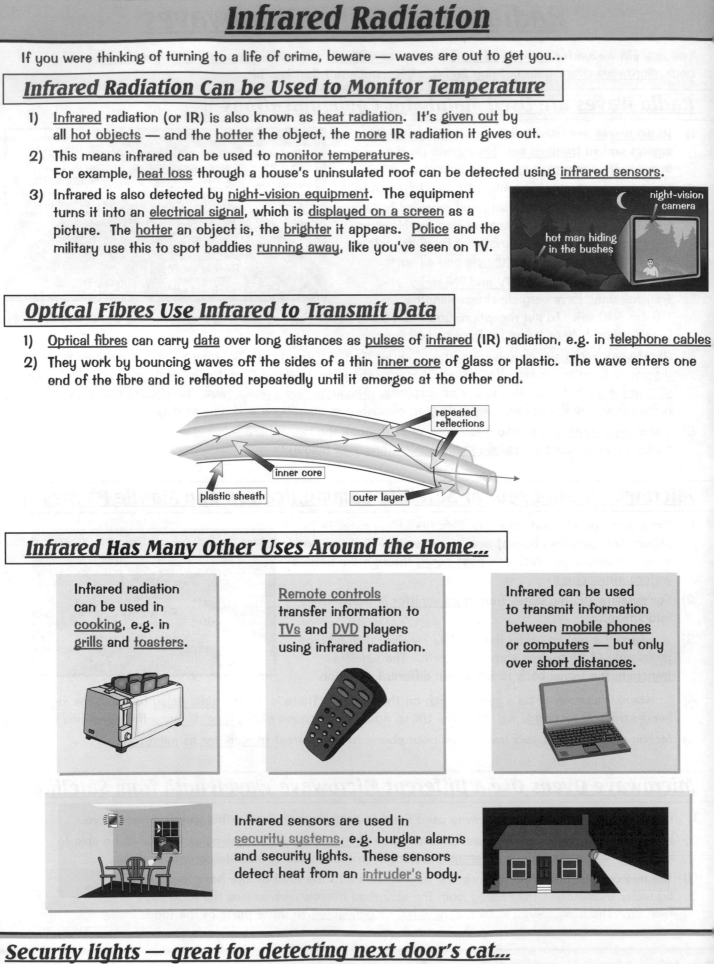

night-vision camera

hot man hiding in the bushes

Optical Fibres Use Infrared to Transmit Data

1) <u>Optical fibres</u> can carry <u>data</u> over long distances as <u>pulses</u> of <u>infrared</u> (IR) radiation, e.g. in <u>telephone cables</u>.

2) They work by bouncing waves off the sides of a thin <u>inner core</u> of glass or plastic. The wave enters one end of the fibre and is reflected repeatedly until it emerges at the other end.

repeated reflections

inner core

plastic sheath

outer layer

Infrared Has Many Other Uses Around the Home...

Infrared radiation can be used in <u>cooking</u>, e.g. in <u>grills</u> and <u>toasters</u>.

<u>Remote controls</u> transfer information to <u>TVs</u> and <u>DVD</u> players using infrared radiation.

Infrared can be used to transmit information between <u>mobile phones</u> or <u>computers</u> — but only over <u>short distances</u>.

Infrared sensors are used in <u>security systems</u>, e.g. burglar alarms and security lights. These sensors detect heat from an <u>intruder's</u> body.

Security lights — great for detecting next door's cat...

Optical fibres are a good way to send data over long distances — the EM waves travel fast, and they can't easily be tapped into or suffer interference (unlike a signal that's <u>broadcast</u> from a transmitter, like radio). The signals do need occasional boosting — some of the IR radiation gets lost because of imperfections in the fibre.

Visible Light, UV and X-rays

You might already know about some of these uses of light, UV and X rays. But you need to know it all...

We Need Visible Light to See

It might seem pretty obvious, but we only see objects because they're <u>illuminated</u> — they either <u>give out</u> or <u>reflect</u> light. For you to see an object, light needs to <u>enter</u> your eyes. Duh.

1) When light enters your eye, it gets <u>refracted</u> (see page 12) through the lens and <u>focused</u> onto the retina at the back of the eye. The retina then sends <u>messages</u> to the brain (via the optic nerve), and the <u>very clever</u> brain <u>interprets</u> them. Ta da — you can see.

2) Photography works in a <u>similar</u> way to the eye. Cameras use a <u>lens</u> to focus <u>visible light</u> onto a light-sensitive <u>film</u> or electronic <u>sensor</u> that <u>records</u> the image.

3) The lens's <u>aperture</u> controls <u>how much</u> light enters the camera.

4) The <u>shutter speed</u> determines the <u>how long</u> the film or sensor is <u>exposed</u> to the light.

5) By varying the <u>aperture</u> and <u>shutter speed</u>, a photographer can capture as much or as little light as they want in their photograph.

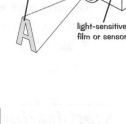

lens
subject
light-sensitive film or sensor

Ultraviolet Radiation is Used to Detect Forged Bank Notes

1) <u>Fluorescence</u> is a property of certain chemicals, where <u>ultraviolet radiation (UV)</u> is <u>absorbed</u> and then <u>visible light</u> is <u>emitted</u>. That's why fluorescent colours look so <u>bright</u> — they do actually <u>emit light</u>.

2) <u>Banks</u> now print <u>special markings</u> in <u>fluorescent ink</u> on their <u>bank notes</u> to detect <u>forgeries</u>. <u>Under a UV light</u>, <u>genuine</u> notes will <u>display</u> the <u>special fluorescent markings</u>... <u>Fake</u> notes, on the other hand, are often printed on <u>cheaper paper</u> that's <u>slightly fluorescent</u>, so under UV, they'll <u>glow all over</u>, and there'll be <u>no markings</u>.

3) Here, it's the amount of radiation <u>emitted</u> that you're detecting and measuring.

4) <u>Fluorescent lamps</u> (like the ones you might have in your <u>classroom</u>) use UV radiation to <u>emit</u> visible light. They're <u>safe</u> to use as <u>all</u> the UV radiation is <u>absorbed</u> by a phosphor coating on the inside of the glass.

5) <u>Security pens</u> can be used to <u>mark</u> your property with your name (e.g. laptops). The ink in the pen is only visible in <u>UV light</u> — this can help the police <u>identify</u> your property if it's stolen.

6) UV radiation can also be used to <u>disinfect water</u> — the UV <u>kills off</u> any viruses and bacteria in the water, making it <u>safer</u> to use.

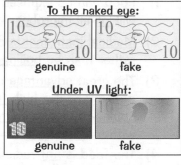

To the naked eye:
genuine   fake
Under UV light:
genuine   fake

X-Rays are Used to Look Inside Objects

1) <u>Radiographers</u> in <u>hospitals</u> take <u>X-ray 'photographs'</u> of people to see if they have any <u>broken bones</u>.

2) X-rays pass <u>easily through flesh</u> but not so easily through <u>denser material</u> like <u>bones</u> or <u>metal</u>. So it's the amount of radiation that's <u>absorbed</u> (or <u>not absorbed</u>) that gives you an X-ray image.

3) X-rays can cause <u>cancer</u>, so radiographers wear <u>lead aprons</u> and stand behind a <u>lead screen</u> or <u>leave the room</u> to keep their <u>exposure</u> to X-rays to a <u>minimum</u>.

4) Airport security use X-rays to scan <u>luggage</u> to check for suspicious-looking objects.

5) Some airports now use X-ray scanners on <u>passengers</u> to look for concealed weapons or explosives — low-level X-rays are used so they <u>aren't</u> as harmful as the X-rays used in <u>hospitals</u>.

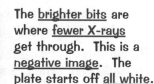

The <u>brighter bits</u> are where <u>fewer X-rays</u> get through. This is a <u>negative image</u>. The plate starts off <u>all white</u>.

Don't lie to an X-ray — they can see right through you...

Pretty interesting stuff, this, I reckon. All the waves on this page are types of EM waves. You don't need to understand all the ins and outs of EM waves for this little bit — it's more the idea of how they can be used.

Gamma Rays and Ionising Radiation

Gamma rays may be one <u>cause</u> of cancer — but they also have some important uses...

Radiotherapy — the Treatment of Cancer Using γ-Rays

1) Since high doses of gamma rays will <u>kill all living cells</u>, they can be used to <u>treat cancers</u>.

2) The gamma rays have to be <u>directed carefully</u> and at just the right <u>dosage</u> so as to kill the <u>cancer cells</u> without killing too many <u>normal cells</u>.

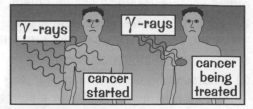

3) However, a <u>fair bit of damage</u> is <u>inevitably</u> done to <u>normal cells</u>, which makes the patient feel <u>very ill</u>. But if the cancer is <u>successfully killed off</u> in the end, then it's worth it.

4) Gamma rays can also be used to <u>diagnose</u> cancer. A <u>radioactive isotope</u> is injected into the patient — a gamma camera is then used to detect where the radioactive isotope travels in the body. This creates an <u>image</u> which can then be used to <u>detect</u> where there might be cancer.

Sterilisation of Food and Surgical Instruments Uses γ-Rays

1) <u>Food</u> can be exposed to a <u>high dose</u> of <u>gamma rays</u> which will <u>kill</u> all <u>microbes</u>, keeping the food <u>fresh for longer</u>.

2) <u>Medical instruments</u> can be <u>sterilised</u> in just the same way, rather than by <u>boiling them</u>.

3) The great <u>advantage</u> of <u>irradiation</u> over boiling is that it doesn't involve <u>high temperatures</u>, so things like <u>fresh apples</u> or <u>plastic instruments</u> can be totally <u>sterilised</u> without <u>damaging</u> them.

4) The food is <u>not</u> radioactive afterwards, so it's <u>perfectly safe</u> to eat.

5) The radioactive isotope used for this needs to be a <u>very strong</u> emitter of <u>gamma rays</u>.

Gamma Radiation is One of the Three Types of Ionising Radiation

The other two types of ionising radiation are <u>alpha</u> (α) and <u>beta</u> (β).

1) Ionising radiation is <u>emitted</u> all the time by <u>radioactive sources</u> when their nuclei <u>decay</u>.

2) This emission is completely <u>random</u> and so you <u>can't</u> predict when it'll happen for a given nucleus — but when it does, it'll <u>spit out</u> one or more of the three types of ionising radiation (<u>alpha</u>, <u>beta</u> and <u>gamma</u>).

3) All three types <u>transfer energy</u> — that's why they're called <u>ionising radiation</u>. They're so energetic that they <u>bash</u> into atoms and <u>knock</u> electrons off them.

4) Alpha, beta and gamma all have their own <u>uses</u> — but they can also be <u>very</u> dangerous. For example, if radiation enters your body it will <u>collide</u> with molecules in your cells. These collisions cause <u>ionisation</u>, which <u>damages</u> or <u>destroys</u> the molecules — which can lead to <u>cancer</u>.

Learn your alphabet-agamma...

It's quite difficult to do research on how radiation affects humans. This is partly because it would be very <u>unethical</u> to do <u>controlled experiments</u>, exposing people to huge doses of radiation just to see what happens. We rely mostly on studies of populations affected by <u>nuclear accidents</u> or nuclear <u>bombs</u>.

The Solar System

Our Solar System is made up of the Sun, orbited by the planets Mercury, Venus, Earth, Mars, Jupiter, Saturn, Uranus and Neptune. Oh, and an asteroid belt chucked in for good measure between Mars and Jupiter.

Planets Reflect Sunlight and Orbit the Sun in Ellipses

1) You can see some planets with the naked eye. They look like stars, but they're totally different.

2) All planets orbit around stars.

3) Planets often have moons orbiting around them. Moons are usually much smaller than their planets, and found pretty close to the planet.

Our Solar System

Remember we see stars because they give out light.

4) In the diagram below, the sizes of the Moon, Earth and Sun are to scale. But there's only room on the page to show about 1° of the Sun's circumference — it's so enormous compared to the planets.

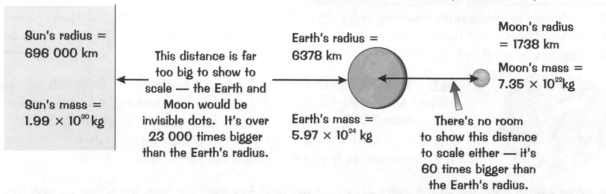

Sun's radius = 696 000 km

Sun's mass = 1.99×10^{30} kg

This distance is far too big to show to scale — the Earth and Moon would be invisible dots. It's over 23 000 times bigger than the Earth's radius.

Earth's radius = 6378 km

Earth's mass = 5.97×10^{24} kg

Moon's radius = 1738 km

Moon's mass = 7.35×10^{22} kg

There's no room to show this distance to scale either — it's 60 times bigger than the Earth's radius.

5) The planets in our Solar System vary massively in size. Mercury, the smallest planet, has a radius 285 times smaller than the Sun's. Even the biggest planet, Jupiter, has a radius 10 times smaller than the Sun's.

6) Neptune is the furthest planet from the Sun — it's about 30 times further from the Sun than the Earth is.

7) Manned spacecraft can reach the moon in 3 days and one could potentially reach Mars in around 9 months. A manned spacecraft to Neptune would take at least 12 years — and that's only one-way. Eek.

Our Sun is in the Milky Way Galaxy

1) A galaxy is a collection of billions of stars. The Sun is one of many billions of stars which form the Milky Way galaxy.

2) The distance between neighbouring stars is often hundreds of thousands of times greater than the distance between planets in our Solar System. After the Sun, the nearest star to us is 4×10^{13} km away.

3) There are billions of galaxies which all make up the Universe.

4) The distance between galaxies is often millions of times greater than the distance between the stars inside a galaxy.

5) No one is really sure how big the Universe is. We do know that the light from the most distant galaxies (that we can see) takes billions of years to reach us.

6) Compare that with the fact that light takes about 500 seconds to reach us on Earth from the Sun — and you'll maybe get a bit more of an idea how ENORMOUS the Universe really is.

You are here

For really big distances like this, astronomers sometimes use the units of light years. 1 light year (ly) is the distance that light would travel through a vacuum in one year. 1 ly = 9.5×10^{12} km

Revision's hard work — you've got to plan et...

Scientists have always argued about what makes a planet a planet, but they finally decided in 2006. So, is Pluto a planet? It's much smaller than the others, has a different orbit, and a moon almost as big as itself. And what about this 10th 'planet' discovered recently (2003 UB$_{313}$, or 'Eris' to its mates), which is bigger than Pluto, but has an even weirder orbit? No and no... apparently. So there you go.

Is Anybody Out There?

If you want to find out about whether there is <u>life beyond Earth</u>, you could get in a spaceship and go out into the Universe to see — but that's pretty difficult, expensive and <u>dangerous</u>. There are easier ways...

Some Scientists are Looking for Signs of Life

1) Many scientists want to try and find out if there's <u>life</u> out there. Space exploration is very <u>expensive</u>, and <u>impractical</u> for anything beyond the Solar System — the distances are just too large. Scientists usually use <u>Earth-based telescopes</u> or other <u>remote-sensing</u> techniques to get some initial clues — before they spend loads of money sending robots or people for a closer look.

2) Scientists haven't found anything exciting, but they are using these methods to search for planets with <u>suitable conditions</u> for life.

SETI Looks for Radio Signals from Other Planets

1) Us Earthlings are constantly beaming <u>radio</u>, <u>TV</u> and <u>radar</u> into space for any passing aliens to detect. There might be life out there that's as clever as we are. Or even more clever. They may have built <u>transmitters</u> to send out signals like ours.

2) <u>SETI</u> stands for Search for ExtraTerrestrial Intelligence. Scientists on the SETI project are looking for <u>narrow bands</u> of <u>radio wavelengths</u> coming to Earth from outer space. They're looking for <u>meaningful signals</u> in all the '<u>noise</u>'.

3) Signals in a narrow band <u>could</u> have come from a <u>transmitter</u>. The 'noise' comes from other things like giant stars.

4) It takes <u>ages</u> to analyse all the radio waves, so the SETI folk get help from the public — you can download a <u>screensaver</u> off the Internet which analyses a chunk of radio waves.

5) SETI has been going for about <u>50 years</u> but they've <u>not found anything</u>. Not a sausage. ☹

6) Scientists are now looking for possible <u>laser</u> signals from outer space. Watch this space...

Robots and Probes Can Collect Data and Samples

Scientists sometimes send <u>spacecraft</u> to try and collect evidence of life.

1) Spacecraft carrying probes have been sent to investigate <u>planets</u> and <u>moons</u> in our Solar System, such as <u>Mars</u> and <u>Titan</u> (one of Saturn's moons). These <u>probes</u> carry instruments which can <u>continuously record data</u> about conditions, e.g. temperature. All this data is sent back to Earth on microwave or radio signals.

2) <u>Robots</u>, like the 1976 <u>Mars Viking landers</u>, can take <u>photos</u> and <u>collect</u> soil and rock <u>samples</u> to analyse. The landers took soil <u>samples</u> using a robotic arm and carried out <u>experiments</u> on the soil to see if they could find any signs of life, e.g. <u>bacteria</u> — the results were sent to Earth using <u>radio signals</u>.

3) Robots don't do <u>all</u> the hard work though. Scientists still have to work out <u>what the data means</u> — for instance, this photograph from a meteorite from Mars <u>could</u> be evidence that life exists (or has existed) on Mars, but it <u>could</u> be lots of other things.

This <u>could</u> be a microscopic fossil of a bacterium-like organism from Mars...

500 nm

Then again, it could be a crystal, some bits of metal or the remains of last night's curry...

4) Scientists don't just look for life on other planets — they look at <u>comets</u> and <u>asteroids</u> too. In 2003, the <u>Hayabusa Spacecraft</u> was sent to collect a sample of <u>dust</u> from a nearby <u>asteroid</u>. This was the first ever attempt to send a spacecraft that would collect an asteroid sample and then <u>bring it back</u> to Earth for analysis.

Intelligent life — don't flatter yourself...

Science fiction aside, we haven't really found that much yet. But you can see why they keep trying — it's such a tantalising thought. Other beings on another planet at the other side of the Universe... Would they be trying to discover US? If we found each other, could we communicate? Blows my mind.

Looking into Space

There are various objects in space, and they emit or reflect different frequencies of EM radiation. And that can be really useful to help us find out what's going on 'out there'.

Space Telescopes Have a Clearer View Than Those on Earth

Telescopes help you to see distant objects clearly. But there can be problems...

1) If you're trying to detect light, Earth's atmosphere gets in the way — it absorbs a lot of the light coming from space before it can reach us. To observe the frequencies absorbed, you have to go above the atmosphere.

2) Then there's pollution. Light pollution (light thrown up into the sky from street lamps, etc.) makes it hard to pick out dim objects. And air pollution (e.g. dust particles) can reflect and absorb light coming from space. So to get the best view possible from Earth, a telescope should be on top of a mountain (where there's less atmosphere above it), and far away from any cities (e.g. on Hawaii).

Night sky in rural area with no light pollution.   Night sky in urban area with light pollution.

3) But to avoid the problem of the atmosphere, the thing to do is put your telescope in space, away from the mist and murk down here. The first space telescope (called Hubble) was launched by NASA in 1990. It can see objects that are about a billion times fainter than you can see unaided from Earth.

Different Telescopes Detect Different Types of EM Wave

To get as full a picture of the Universe as possible, you need to detect different kinds of EM wave.

1) The earliest telescopes were all optical telescopes which detect visible light. They're used to look at objects close by and in other galaxies. But many objects in the Universe aren't detectable using visible light — so other types of EM telescopes are needed to observe them.

2) From the 1940s onwards, telescopes were developed for all parts of the EM spectrum. These modern telescopes mean we can now 'see' parts of the Universe that we couldn't see before and learn more about the Universe, e.g. its structure.

3) Cygnus A is a nearby galaxy. When you look at it through an optical telescope, you see the galaxy as a small blob, surrounded by stars. When observed using a radio telescope instead, you see two 'radio jets' moving away from the centre of the galaxy in opposite directions — these create two massive 'lobes' of hot radiation. Impressive stuff.

An image of Cygnus A using an optical telescope.   An image of Cygnus A using a radio telescope.

NRAO/AUI/NSF/SCIENCE PHOTO LIBRARY

4) X-ray telescopes are a good way to 'see' violent, high-temperature events in space, like exploding stars.

5) Radio telescopes were responsible for the discovery of the cosmic microwave background radiation (p.26) — this helped scientists to learn more about the origins of the Universe.

6) Telescopes are improving all the time — bigger telescopes give us better resolution (i.e. a lot of detail) and can gather more light, so we can see things we couldn't before as they were too faint. Improved magnification means we can now look further into space — more and more galaxies are being discovered.

7) Discovering more galaxies is important to help scientists learn more about their life cycle. Some pictures taken by the Hubble Space Telescope show galaxies at all different stages of their life. These images are used to help scientists learn more about how galaxies are formed and how they evolve.

8) Modern telescopes often work alongside computers. Computers help create clearer and sharper images and make it easy to capture these pictures so they can be analysed later.

9) Computers make it possible to collect and store huge amounts of data, 24 hours a day, without having to rely on humans. They also make it easier and quicker to analyse all this data.

Telescope broken — we can't get the van up there, mate...

Most telescopes contain a lot of delicate, easily damaged parts. This is why it's so expensive to put them in space (as well as the cost of launching the rocket) — they've got to be strong enough to withstand all the shaking on board the vehicle which takes them into orbit, but they need to be lightweight too. It's hard work being a boffin.

Space and Spectrometry

It's alright learning about all this space stuff — but it's important to get a bit of real-life practice to help you understand it all too. Luckily this page ticks both those boxes — the good times are a-comin'.

Most Large Optical Telescopes Have Spectrometers

An example of an absorption spectrum

A spectrometer is a tool used to analyse the light given out by stars and galaxies.

1) Very simply, it works by the telescope directing a beam of light into the spectrometer and through a slit. This diffracts the light and splits it up into a spectrum — similar to a prism (p.15).

2) The light spectra from stars and galaxies contain dark lines (see picture).

3) These dark lines are caused by the light at those wavelengths being absorbed, e.g. by elements in the star's atmosphere. These patterns of dark lines are called absorption spectra.

dark lines

4) Absorption spectra can be used to work out what the stars and galaxies are made of — each element has its own particular absorption spectrum.

5) For example, the absorption spectrum you'd see when looking at light from our Sun is very similar to the one you'd see when looking at light from a hydrogen lamp. Which makes sense as the Sun is mostly made of hydrogen.

6) Some spectra have bright lines — these are emission spectra. The lines are caused by extra light being emitted at those wavelengths. Emission spectra can also be used to work out what something is made of.

7) The spectra for galaxies further away appear more red than they should (see page 26).

You Can Make a Simple Spectrometer Using a CD

You can analyse the spectra of some common everyday light sources by making a spectrometer. You just need a cardboard box, a CD (or DVD) and some scissors:

1) Make a slit about 1 mm wide on one end of the box — this is where the light will come through.

2) Then make a slit for the CD at a 45° angle on the side of the box shown in the diagram.

3) Now make a hole to look through (see diagram) by cutting a slot about 2 cm by 6 cm.

4) Put the CD into the box so that the underside of the CD (the "rainbow" side) is facing where you'll look through.

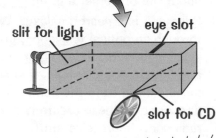

slit for light   eye slot

slot for CD

5) Then hold up the box so that it lets in light from your source through the slit — you should be able to see the visible spectrum. (Make sure you do this in a darkened room — so the only light getting into the box is that from your source.)

Watch out — if your slot is bigger than 1 mm your spectrum will be blurry and if it's too small it won't be very bright.

6) Experimenting with different sources of light will show different looking spectra. Ordinary light bulbs, sodium lamps and a white page on a computer screen are good ones to try out.

7) What you'll see using your spectrometer won't look exactly the same as the picture of the absorption spectrum at the top of the page. That's because this is a pretty basic spectrometer. Here are a few pictures to show you the sort of thing you might be able to see:

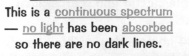

ordinary light bulb

sodium lamp (e.g. a street lamp)

white page on a laptop screen

This is a continuous spectrum — no light has been absorbed so there are no dark lines.

The bright lines show the wavelengths of light emitted, the dark lines show the wavelengths that weren't emitted.

Looking at light from stars and galaxies — it's a spectra-cle

Spectrometry is a clever thing. It's quite a simple idea, but it's made a huge impact on our understanding of the Universe. In fact, most of what we know about what makes up our solar system is because of spectrometry. And to think, you now have the skills to spectrometry away in the comfort of your own home. Splendid. And if you're really interested, look up 'line spectra' on the Internet — you'll see lots more pretty pics of spectra.

The Life Cycle of Stars

Stars go through many traumatic stages in their lives — just like teenagers.

Nebula

1) Stars initially form from clouds of dust and gas called NEBULAS.

2) The force of gravity makes the gas and dust spiral in together. Gravitational energy is converted into heat energy, so the temperature rises.

3) When the temperature gets high enough, hydrogen nuclei undergo thermonuclear fusion to form helium nuclei and give out massive amounts of energy. A star is born. It immediately enters a long stable period where the heat created by the nuclear fusion provides an outward pressure to balance the force of gravity pulling everything inwards. In this stable period it's called a MAIN SEQUENCE STAR and it can last for several billion years. (The Sun is in the middle of this stable period — or to put it another way, the Earth has already had half its innings before the Sun engulfs it.)

Main Sequence Star

4) Eventually the hydrogen in the core begins to run out and the star then swells into a RED GIANT (it becomes red because the surface cools).

Red Giant

Small stars

Big stars

5) A small-to-medium-sized star like the Sun then becomes unstable and ejects its outer layer of dust and gas as a planetary nebula.

planetary nebula.... and a White Dwarf

6) This leaves behind a hot, dense solid core — a WHITE DWARF, which just cools down and eventually disappears. (That's going to be really sad.)

Neutron Star...

...or Black Hole

Supernova

7) Big stars, however, start to glow brightly again as they undergo more fusion and expand and contract several times, forming heavier elements in various nuclear reactions. Eventually they'll explode in a SUPERNOVA.

8) The exploding supernova throws the outer layers of dust and gas into space, leaving a very dense core called a NEUTRON STAR. If the star is big enough this will become a BLACK HOLE.

Red Giants, White Dwarfs, Black Holes, Green Ghosts...

Erm. Now how do they know that exactly... Anyway, now you know what the future holds — our Sun is going to fizzle out, and it'll just get very very cold and very very dark. Great. On a brighter note, the Sun's got a good few years in it yet, so it's still worth passing those exams.

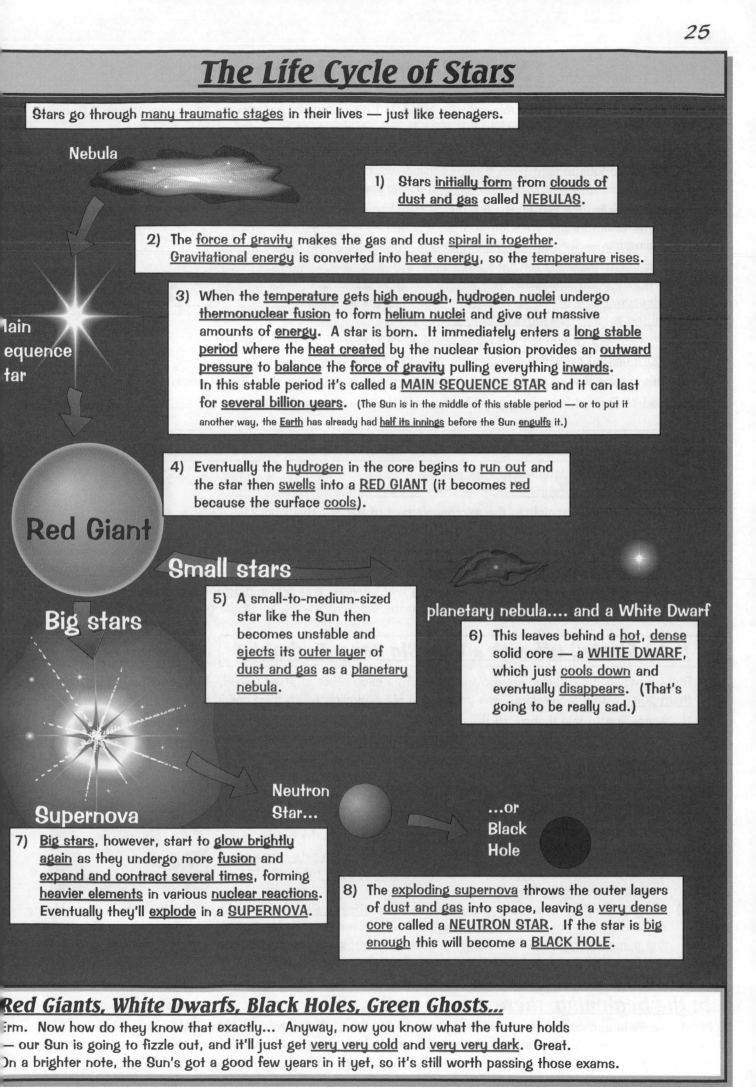

The Origins of the Universe

Once upon a time, there was a really Big Bang — that's the most convincing theory we've got.

Light from Other Galaxies is Red-Shifted

1) When we look at light from distant galaxies we find that the frequencies are all lower than they should be — they're shifted towards the red end of the spectrum.

2) This is called the red-shift. It's the same effect as the 'vrrr-oomm' from a racing car — the engine noise sounds lower-pitched when the car's gone past you and is moving away from you.

① The sound waves from a stationary car are equally spaced, like this
② But for a moving car, the wavelengths seem longer here...
...than here
③ So the frequency of the sound waves seems to be lower if the car is moving away from you.

3) Measurements of red-shift suggest that all the galaxies are moving away from us very quickly — and it's the same result whichever direction you look in.

4) More distant galaxies have greater red-shifts than nearer ones.

5) This means that more distant galaxies are moving away faster than nearer ones.

6) Red-shift provides evidence that the whole Universe is expanding.

There's a Uniform Microwave Radiation from All Directions

1) Scientists have detected low frequency electromagnetic radiation coming from all parts of the Universe.

2) This radiation is mainly in the microwave part of the EM spectrum. It's known as the cosmic microwave background radiation (CMB radiation).

3) For complicated reasons, CMB radiation is strong evidence for an initial Big Bang, and as the Universe expands and cools, this background radiation 'cools' and drops in frequency.

4) The Big Bang is currently the only theory that provides any explanation for CMB radiation. The discovery of the CMB radiation led to the Big Bang theory being the currently accepted model.

It All Started Off with a Very Big Bang (Probably)

Right now, all the galaxies are moving away from each other at great speed. But something must have got them going. That 'something' was probably a big explosion — so they called it the Big Bang...

1) According to this theory, all the matter and energy in the Universe must have been compressed into a very small space. Then it exploded and started expanding.

2) The expansion is still going on. We can use the current rate of expansion of the Universe to estimate its age. Our best guess is that the Big Bang happened about 14 billion years ago.

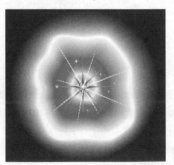

3) These estimates might not be very accurate, partly because it's hard to tell how much the expansion has slowed down since the Big Bang.

4) Without gravity the Universe would expand at the same rate forever. But as it is, all the masses in the Universe attract each other — and tend to slow the expansion down.

5) The Big Bang isn't the only game in town. The 'Steady State' theory says that the Universe has always existed as it is now, and it always will do. It's based on the idea that the Universe appears pretty much the same everywhere. This theory explains the apparent expansion (and red-shift) by suggesting that matter is being created in the spaces as the Universe expands.

In the beginning, there was — well, nobody knows, actually...

Most scientists accept the idea of the Big Bang — it's the best way to explain the evidence we have at the moment. But if new evidence turns up, the theory could turn out to be rubbish. After all, there wasn't anyone around 14 billion years ago, taking photos and writing things down in a little notebook.

Revision Summary for P1a Topics 1, 2 & 3

There's been loads of information over the last three topics. And there is really only one way to check
that you've learnt it all — you guessed it, a page full of questions. So go on, have a go...

1) Describe the main features of the geocentric model.
2) Explain how Galileo's observations of Jupiter proved the geocentric model wrong.
3) How are we able to see stars? How are we able to see planets?
4)* Find the wavelength of a wave with frequency 15 MHz and speed 3 x 10^8 m/s.
5) Give an example of a transverse wave. Give an example of a longitudinal wave.
6) Light is reflected off a mirror, as shown in the diagram. What is the angle a?
7) Describe, using a diagram, what happens to a light ray as it travels from air into water at an angle.
8) Draw a diagram to show how a converging lens works.
9) Describe what is meant by the focal point of a lens. How can you work out the focal length of a lens?
10) Briefly explain how an object's distance from a lens affects what image you will see.
11) How many converging lenses does a refracting telescope use? Explain how a refracting telescope works.
12) Draw a diagram to show how a concave mirror reflects light.
13) Explain how a reflecting telescope works.
14) List the seven types of electromagnetic radiation in order of increasing wavelength.
15) Which type of electromagnetic radiation has the highest frequency?
16) Briefly describe how Herschel discovered infrared radiation.
17) Explain why some people are worried about the effects of using mobile phones.
18) What can too much exposure to UV radiation cause? Give three ways to protect yourself from UV rays.
19) Explain why hilly areas often get poor TV and radio reception.
20) Briefly explain how an optical fibre works.
21) List five uses of infrared radiation around the home.
22) Describe briefly what happens when UV light shines on a fluorescent material.
23) Describe how X-ray imaging can help to find a fracture in someone's bone.
24) Explain why radiotherapy treatment is directed carefully only at the tumour.
25) Give one advantage of irradiating food with gamma rays over other methods of sterilising.
26) Name the three types of ionising radiation. What is ionising radiation emitted from?
27) Compare the distance between the Sun and Earth with the distance between the Earth and Moon.
28) What is a galaxy? Describe the scale of the distance between galaxies.
29) What does SETI stand for?
30) Suggest one type of information a space probe might collect.
31) Give two disadvantages of telescopes on Earth compared with space telescopes.
32) Explain why we need telescopes for other parts of the EM spectrum, as well as visible light.
33) Describe what an absorption spectrum looks like. Why does it look like this?
34) Describe the first stages of a star's formation. Where does the initial energy come from?
35) What is a 'main sequence' star? How long does it last? What happens after that?
36) What are the final two stages of a small star's life? What are the two final stages of a big star's life?
37) Explain what red-shift is. Do galaxies further away have more or less red-shift than those nearer?
38) What's the main theory for the origin of the Universe? Give two important bits of evidence for it.

Ultrasound and Infrasound

Can you hear that? If not, 'that' could be ultrasound or infrasound...

Ultrasound is Sound with Frequencies Higher Than 20 000 Hz

Electrical devices can be made which produce electrical oscillations of any frequency. These can easily be converted into mechanical vibrations to produce sound waves beyond the range of human hearing (i.e. frequencies above 20 000 Hz). This is called ultrasound and it pops up all over the place.

Ultrasound Waves Get Partially Reflected at a Boundary Between Media

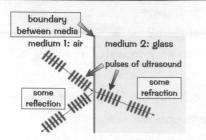

boundary between media
medium 1: air   medium 2: glass
pulses of ultrasound
some refraction
some reflection

1) When a wave passes from one medium into another, some of the wave is reflected off the boundary between the two media, and some is transmitted (and refracted). This is partial reflection.

2) What this means is that you can point a pulse of ultrasound at an object, and wherever there are boundaries between one substance and another, some of the ultrasound gets reflected back.

3) The time it takes for the reflections to reach a detector can be used to measure how far away the boundary is (see next page).

Ultrasound is Useful in Lots of Different Ways

Pre-natal scanning of a foetus

1) Ultrasound waves can pass through the body, but whenever they reach a boundary between two different media (like fluid in the womb and the skin of the foetus) some of the wave is reflected back and detected.

2) The exact timing and distribution of these echoes are processed by a computer to produce a video image of the foetus.

3) No one knows for sure whether ultrasound is safe in all cases but X-rays would definitely be dangerous to the foetus.

Saline gel   ULTRASONIC SCANNER   Reflected waves detected
Foetus

Sonar

1) Boats and submarines use sonar to detect stuff in the water around them.

2) They emit waves of ultrasound which reflect off things like other boats, the sea bed and marine animals — and detect these reflected waves as they arrive back at the boat.

3) Computers on-board time the delay between emitting the waves and detecting their reflections, and then calculate how far away the other objects are.

4) Animals like bats and dolphins use ultrasound to sense their way around their environment in a similar way.

5) Many animals (e.g. frogs, insects, whales and even rats) also use ultrasound frequencies to communicate with one another.

Infrasound is Sound with Frequencies Less Than 20 Hz

1) Sound that has a frequency below the range of human hearing (i.e. below 20 Hz) is called infrasound.

2) Because infrasound waves have long wavelengths, they can travel long distances and diffract around objects easily.

3) Elephants use infrasound to communicate with other members of their herd over long distances. Tigers also use infrasound in their growls and roars so they can be heard by rivals or mates from far away.

4) Some microphones are sensitive enough to detect infrasound and can be used to monitor animal movements in remote locations.

5) Meteor strikes and volcanic eruptions produce infrasound which can be used to detect them from far away.

Barry White — the undisputed master of the low frequency note...

Remember — infrasound has a frequency below 20 Hz and ultrasound has a frequency above 20 kHz. Make sure you learn and understand the uses on this page too, and the exam questions on this stuff should be a doddle.

Calculating Distances Using Ultrasound

Ultrasound waves can be used to work out distances. And I'm not just telling you that as a mildly interesting fact — you might have to do it in your exam. So here are some helpful examples.

Speed = Distance ÷ Time... and DON'T FORGET the FACTOR OF 2

This is about the easiest formula in Physics. If you don't know it by now... well, you ought to.

$$\text{wave speed (m/s)} = \frac{\text{distance (m)}}{\text{time (s)}}$$

They'll expect you to be able to use this to find the distance to and from a reflecting surface, if you know both the speed of the wave and how long the wave takes to travel there and back.

EXAMPLE: A pulse of ultrasound takes 4.5 seconds to travel from a submarine to the sea bed and back again.

If the speed of sound in seawater is 1520 m/s, how far away is the submarine from the sea bed?

ANSWER: The formula is of course "speed = distance ÷ time" or "s = x ÷ t". We want to find the distance, x. We already know the time, 4.5 s, and the speed of sound in seawater, 1520 m/s, hence x = s × t (from the triangle).

This gives: x = 1520 × 4.5 = <u>6840 m</u>... But watch out! <u>Don't forget the factor of two for reflection questions</u>: The 4.5 s is for <u>there and back</u>, so the sea bed is only <u>half</u> that distance away, <u>3420 m</u>.

Pulse sent | Pulse back

EXAMPLE: A pregnant woman goes for a prenatal scan. A pulse of ultrasound takes 0.00005 s (0.05 ms) to be sent from a point on her stomach to the baby's head and back again.

Given that the speed of sound inside soft tissue in the body is 1540 m/s, work out the distance of the baby's head from the scanner.

Pulse sent
Pulse back

(See previous page for more on ultrasound scanning.)

ANSWER: Speed of sound inside soft tissue in the body = 1540 m/s
You need the good old formula: speed = distance / time
— and again you have to rearrange it (formula triangle):
So, x = s × t = 1540 × 0.00005 = <u>0.077 m</u>.

But remember — the wave has been <u>reflected</u>, so it's travelled <u>twice the distance</u>. So you need to <u>divide by 2</u>, which gives 0.0385 m = 3.85 cm.

So the head is <u>3.85 cm</u> away from the scanner.

It's only a little maths — it won't hurt a bit...

So, learn the formula, practise rearranging it and remember the factor of 2. Yep, that's about it. Cover the answers to the two examples above and have a go at answering them yourself — but be careful not to have too much fun.

The Earth's Structure

No one accepted the theory of plate tectonics for ages. Almost everyone does now. How times change.

The Earth Has a Crust, Mantle, Outer and Inner Core

The Earth is almost spherical and it has a layered structure, a bit like a scotch egg. Or a peach.

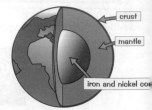

1) The bit we live on, the crust, is very thin (about 20 km).

2) Below that is the mantle. The mantle has all the properties of a solid, except that it can flow very slowly. Within the mantle, radioactive decay takes place (see p.63). This produces a lot of heat, which causes the mantle to flow in convection currents.

3) At the centre of the Earth is the core, which we think is made of iron and nickel. The inner core is solid but the outer core surrounding it is a liquid.

The Earth's Surface is Made Up of Tectonic Plates

1) The crust and the upper part of the mantle are cracked into a number of large pieces called tectonic plates. These plates are a bit like big rafts that 'float' on the mantle.

2) The plates don't stay in one place though. That's because the convection currents in the mantle cause the plates to drift.

3) Most of the plates are moving at speeds of a few cm per year relative to each other.

4) At plate boundaries, the plates may slide past each other — which sometimes causes earthquakes.

It's Difficult to Predict Earthquakes and Tsunami Waves

1) Some countries are particularly susceptible to earthquakes, which can also sometimes cause giant waves called tsunamis. Both can be extremely destructive, especially in areas where the housing isn't built to withstand them. So it would be very useful to be able to predict when they're likely to hit.

2) Unfortunately, predicting them's very hard, and scientists aren't agreed on which method works best.

3) Here's an easy experiment to show how unpredictable earthquakes can be:

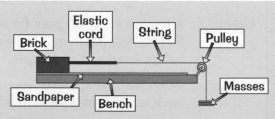

- Fix sandpaper to the surface of a lab bench so that it can't be moved. Place a brick at one end of the bench on top of the sand paper. The brick and sandpaper represent tectonic plates — earthquakes happen when these plates slide suddenly against each other.

- Attach an elastic cord to the brick and join the elastic cord and the string. Tie a mass holder to the end of the string and hang it over a pulley wheel clamped to the bench.

- Gradually add masses to the mass holder. The force of the masses pulling the brick represent the forces of the convection currents in the mantle that make the tectonic plates move.

- As you continue to add masses, the brick will eventually slip to the right — this represents the earthquake.

- The thing is though, if you repeat the experiment using exactly the same equipment, it may take a different number of masses to make the brick slip each time. You can't really predict when it will happen — just like a real earthquake.

4) One way to try and predict earthquakes is to use probabilities based on previous occurrences. E.g. if a city has had earthquakes at regular intervals over the last century, that pattern may continue. This method isn't dead-on accurate, e.g. you might not get an earthquake at the exact location or exact time — maybe it'll be in the next town, or a few months late. But it still gives the area time to prepare, just in case.

Plate Tectonics — it's a smashing theory...

Earthquakes — make sure you know what causes them. And remember, they're rather unpredictable — as that experiment with the brick, the sandpaper, the pulley and the masses shows.

Seismic Waves

You can't drill very far into the Earth's outer layer (only about 12 km), but luckily scientists can use the seismic waves produced by earthquakes to investigate the Earth's inner structure.

Earthquakes and Explosions Cause Seismic Waves

1) When there's an earthquake somewhere, it produces seismic waves which travel out through the Earth. We detect these waves all over the surface of the planet using seismometers.

2) Seismologists work out the time it takes for the shock waves to reach each seismometer.

3) They also note which parts of the Earth don't receive the shock waves at all.

4) There are two different types of seismic waves you need to learn — P waves and S waves:

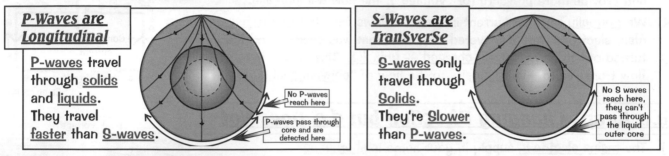

P-Waves are Longitudinal

P-waves travel through solids and liquids. They travel faster than S-waves.

No P-waves reach here

P-waves pass through core and are detected here

S-Waves are TransverSe

S-waves only travel through Solids. They're Slower than P-waves.

No S waves reach here, they can't pass through the liquid outer core

P-waves and S-waves Reflect and Refract

1) When seismic waves reach a boundary between different layers of the Earth, some waves will be reflected.

2) The waves also change speed as the properties (e.g. density) of the mantle and core change. This change in speed causes the waves to change direction — which is refraction, of course (see p.12).

3) Most of the time the waves change speed gradually, resulting in a curved path. But when the properties change suddenly, the wave speed changes abruptly, and the path has a kink.

4) By observing how seismic waves are reflected and refracted, scientists have been able to work out where the properties of the Earth change dramatically. Our current understanding of the internal structure of the Earth is based on these observations.

You Need to Understand the Seismometer Results

1) Seismometer readings (seismograms) can be used to work out the distance to an earthquake's epicentre (the point on the earth's surface directly above the focus of the earthquake).

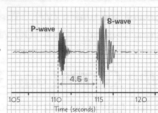

On this seismogram there is a delay of 4.5 seconds between the P-wave and the S-wave.

2) P-waves and S-waves travel at different speeds — so you'll usually see two distinct tremors on the seismogram. The first one is the P-wave and the second is the S-wave (the 'P' and 'S' are for primary and secondary).

3) Using the time difference between the two waves, you can calculate how far away the earthquake or explosion was.

4) Then you can draw a circle on a map centred on the location of your seismometer, with the distance you calculated above as its radius. This is called a distance arc.

5) The distance arcs from three or more seismometers will all cross at one place — this the epicentre of the earthquake. This method of finding the epicentre is called triangulation.

6) Triangulation only works if you have at least three seismometer distance arcs (the distance arcs from two seismometers will cross in two places).

What's that coming straight through the core? Is it a P-wave, Is it a P-wave?

You need to remember that P-waves are longitudinal and S-waves are transverse. You might find it helpful to think of them as Push-waves and Shake-waves. Gosh — what a useful little trick. You can thank me later...

Electric Current and Power

Isn't electricity <u>great</u> — generally, I mean. You can power all sorts of <u>toys and gadgets</u> with electricity. Mind you, it'll be a pain come exam time if you don't know the basics — thankfully they're all on this page.

Electric Current is a Flow of Charge Round a Circuit

1)   <u>CURRENT</u> is the <u>rate of flow of charge</u> around a circuit.
     <u>Electrons</u> usually carry the charge — they're <u>negatively charged</u> particles.

2)   <u>VOLTAGE</u> (or POTENTIAL DIFFERENCE) is an <u>electrical pressure</u> giving a <u>measure</u> of the <u>energy transferred</u>.

3)   That might sound confusing, but try to think of <u>current</u> as like the <u>flow</u> of water around a set of pipes.
     Voltage is like the <u>pressure</u> provided by a <u>pump</u> which pushes the water round — if you <u>turn up the pump</u>
     and provide more <u>pressure</u> (or "<u>voltage</u>"), the flow will <u>increase</u>.

4)   We <u>normally</u> say that current in a circuit flows from <u>positive to negative</u>.
     Alas, electrons were discovered long after that was decided and they
     turned out to be <u>negatively charged</u> — <u>unlucky</u>. This means they <u>actually</u>
     <u>flow</u> from –ve to +ve, <u>opposite</u> to the flow of "<u>conventional current</u>".

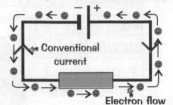
Conventional current · Electron flow

a.c. Keeps Changing Direction but d.c. Does Not

1)   The <u>mains electricity</u> supply in your home is <u>alternating</u>
     <u>current</u> (<u>a.c.</u>). It keeps <u>reversing its direction</u> back and forth.

2)   A CRO can show <u>current</u> as a trace on a graph — an a.c. trace is a <u>wave</u>.

3)   <u>Direct current</u> (<u>d.c.</u>) is <u>different</u>. It <u>always flows</u> in the <u>same direction</u>.

4)   The <u>CRO trace</u> is a <u>horizontal line</u>. The <u>voltage doesn't vary</u> — so the <u>current</u> has a <u>constant</u> value too.

5)   You get <u>direct current</u> from <u>batteries</u> and <u>solar cells</u> (see p.36).

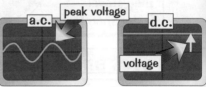
a.c. · peak voltage · d.c. · voltage
Cathode-ray oscilloscope (CRO) traces.

Electrical Power is the Energy Transferred per Second

1)   Electrical appliances are useful because they take in <u>electrical energy</u> and <u>convert it</u> into
     <u>other forms of energy</u>, e.g. a light bulb turns <u>electrical</u> energy into <u>light</u> (and <u>heat</u>) energy.

2)   The electrical <u>power</u> of an appliance tells you how <u>quickly</u> it transfers electrical energy.

> **ELECTRICAL POWER** is the Energy Transferred per Second.

3)   The <u>units</u> of power are watts (W). The <u>higher</u> the power of your appliance, the <u>more energy</u> is
     transferred every second. So a 100 W light bulb is <u>brighter</u> than a 60 W bulb.

Measuring the Current and Voltage Can Tell You the Power

You can calculate the <u>power</u> of any component in a circuit using this nice n' simple experiment:

1)   Make a circuit with an <u>ammeter</u>, <u>switch</u>, <u>battery</u> and your <u>test component</u>
     (e.g. a resistor) in <u>series</u> — this means they're all in <u>one</u> loop.
     The <u>ammeter</u> will measure the <u>current</u> flowing through the circuit.

2)   Connect a <u>voltmeter</u> in <u>parallel</u>, <u>across</u> the component you're
     investigating. The voltmeter will measure the <u>voltage</u> across the component.

3)   Close the switch to <u>complete</u> the circuit — you'll see a <u>reading</u> on
     both the ammeter and voltmeter. <u>Record</u> these numbers then use
     them to calculate the <u>power</u> of the component using this formula:

     battery · switch · test component · V · voltmeter · A · ammeter

> **Power = Current × Voltage**
> (watts, W)   (amps, A)   (volts, V)

$$\frac{P}{I \times V}$$

$$P = I \times V$$

     <u>EXAMPLE</u>: A current of 0.2 A flows through a lamp when it is
     connected to a 3 V battery. Calculate the power of the lamp.
     <u>ANSWER</u>: $P = I \times V = 0.2 \times 3 = \underline{0.6 \text{ W}}$

a.c. = wiggly   d.c. = straight

Learn the differences between a.c. and d.c.. Also, make sure you can spell current correctly.

Generating Electricity

Generators (e.g. in power stations) use something called electromagnetic induction to make electricity. It's a bit mysterious, but don't get bogged down — there's not that much to it.

Moving a Magnet in a Coil of Wire Induces a Voltage

1) You can induce (create) a voltage, and maybe a current, in a conductor by moving a magnet in or near a coil of wire. This is called electromagnetic induction.

2) As you move the magnet, the magnetic field through the coil changes — this change in the magnetic field induces a voltage, and a current flows in the wire (if it's part of a complete circuit).

3) The direction of the voltage and current depends on which way you move the magnet:

If you move the magnet into the coil the voltage and current are induced in the opposite direction from when you move it out of the coil.	If you reverse the magnet's North-South polarity — so that the opposite pole points into the coil, the voltage and current are induced in the opposite direction.

 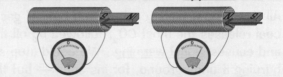

4) You can also create a voltage and current in a conductor by either rotating a magnet in or near a coil of wire, or by rotating a coil of wire in a magnetic field (see below).

Four Factors Affect the Size of the Induced Voltage and Current

1) If you want a bigger peak voltage (and current) you have to increase at least one of these four things:

> 1) The **STRENGTH** of the **MAGNET**   2) The **AREA** of the **COIL**
> 3) The **number of TURNS** on the **COIL**   4) The **SPEED** of movement

2) To reduce the voltage, you would reduce one of those factors, obviously.

3) If you move or turn the magnet faster, you'll get a higher peak voltage, but also get a higher frequency — because the magnetic field is reversing more frequently.

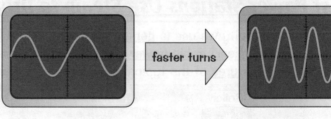

faster turns

This is How All Generators Work

1) Generators generate alternating current (a.c.) by electromagnetic induction, either by rotating a magnet or by rotating a coil of wire and keeping the magnet fixed.

2) All generators just need something to do the turning. That could be anything from a steam-driven turbine (like in a power station) to a water-wheel (like the one the Queen's got in the River Thames to generate electricity for her pad at Windsor).

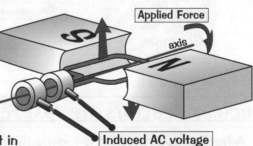

Applied Force

axis

Induced AC voltage

3) A dynamo is a particular type of generator which is often used on bikes to power the lights. Here the magnet is rotated instead of the coil. The dynamo is attached to a wheel — so as you turn the wheels, you're turning the magnet inside the dynamo.

So THAT's how they make electricity — I always wondered...

The National Grid (see p.38) is fed by hundreds of generators — mostly powered by burning things to make steam, which turns a turbine, which turns a coil in a magnetic field. More on that coming up next...

Non-Renewable Energy and Power Stations

There are <u>12</u> different types of <u>energy resource</u>.
They fit into <u>two broad types</u>: <u>renewable</u> and <u>non-renewable</u>.

Non-Renewable Energy Resources Will Run Out One Day

The <u>non-renewables</u> are the <u>three FOSSIL FUELS</u> and <u>NUCLEAR</u>:

1) <u>Coal</u>
2) <u>Oil</u>
3) <u>Natural gas</u>
4) <u>Nuclear fuels</u> (<u>uranium</u> and <u>plutonium</u>)

> a) They will <u>all 'run out'</u> one day.
> b) They all do <u>damage</u> to the environment.
> c) But they provide <u>most of our energy</u>.

There are Environmental Problems with Using Non-Renewables

1) All three <u>fossil fuels</u> (coal, oil and natural gas) release CO_2. For the same amount of energy produced, coal releases the most CO_2, followed by oil then natural gas. All this CO_2 adds to the <u>greenhouse effect</u>, and causes <u>global warming</u>. We could stop some of it entering the atmosphere — by 'capturing' it and <u>burying</u> it underground, for instance — but the technology is too <u>expensive</u> to be widely used yet.

2) Burning coal and oil releases <u>sulfur dioxide</u>, which causes <u>acid rain</u>.
   This is reduced by taking the sulfur out <u>before</u> it's burned, or cleaning up the <u>emissions</u>.

3) <u>Coal mining</u> makes a <u>mess</u> of the <u>landscape</u>, especially "<u>open-cast mining</u>".

4) <u>Oil spillages</u> cause <u>serious environmental problems</u>. We try to avoid them, but they'll always happen.

5) <u>Nuclear power</u> is <u>clean</u> but the <u>nuclear waste</u> is very <u>dangerous</u> and difficult to <u>dispose of</u>.

6) Nuclear <u>fuel</u> (i.e. uranium) is <u>relatively cheap</u> but the <u>overall cost</u> of nuclear power is <u>high</u> due to the cost to <u>build</u> and <u>decommission</u> the <u>power plant</u>.

7) <u>Nuclear power</u> always carries the risk of a <u>major catastrophe</u> like the <u>Chernobyl disaster</u>.

Most Power Stations Use Steam to Drive a Turbine

<u>Most</u> of the electricity we use is <u>generated</u> from the four <u>NON-RENEWABLE</u> sources of energy (<u>coal</u>, <u>oil</u>, <u>natural gas</u> and <u>nuclear</u>) in <u>big power stations</u>, which are all <u>pretty much the same</u> apart from the <u>boiler</u>. <u>Learn</u> the <u>basic features</u> of the typical power station shown here and also the <u>nuclear reactor</u> below.

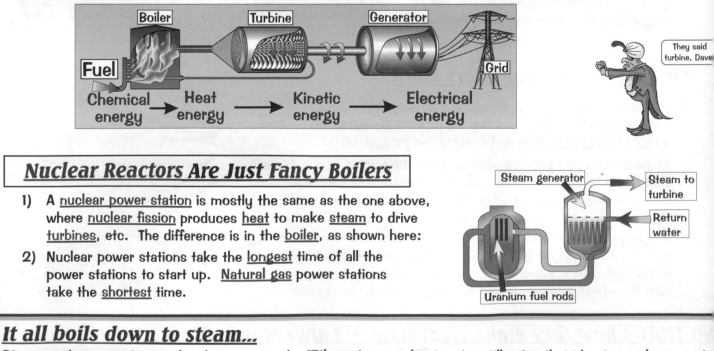

Boiler   Turbine   Generator   Grid

Fuel

Chemical energy → Heat energy → Kinetic energy → Electrical energy

They said turbine, Dave

Nuclear Reactors Are Just Fancy Boilers

1) A <u>nuclear power station</u> is mostly the same as the one above, where <u>nuclear fission</u> produces <u>heat</u> to make <u>steam</u> to drive <u>turbines</u>, etc. The difference is in the <u>boiler</u>, as shown here:

2) Nuclear power stations take the <u>longest</u> time of all the power stations to start up. <u>Natural gas</u> power stations take the <u>shortest</u> time.

Steam generator → Steam to turbine
Return water
Uranium fuel rods

It all boils down to steam...

<u>Steam engines</u> were invented as long ago as the <u>17th century</u>, and yet we're still using that idea to produce most of our electricity today, over <u>300 years</u> later. Amazing...

Using Renewable Energy Resources

Renewable energy sources could solve all our problems when the fossil fuels <u>run out</u> — but there are lots of them to remember. Here are a couple of pages to talk you through the <u>important</u> ones. Enjoy.

Renewable Energy Resources Will Never Run Out

a) A <u>renewable energy source</u> is one that will <u>never run out</u>.

b) Most of them do <u>damage the environment</u>, but in <u>less nasty</u> ways than non-renewables.

c) Sadly they <u>don't all provide much energy</u> and some of them are <u>unreliable</u> as they depend on the <u>weather</u>.

Hydroelectricity — Building Dams and Flooding Valleys

1) <u>Hydroelectric power</u> usually involves <u>flooding</u> a <u>valley</u> by building a <u>big dam</u>.

2) <u>Rainwater</u> is caught and allowed out <u>through turbines</u>.

3) There is a <u>big impact</u> on the <u>environment</u> due to the flooding of the valley and possible <u>loss of habitat</u> for some species.

4) A <u>big advantage</u> is <u>immediate response</u> to increased electricity demand — <u>more</u> water can be let out through the turbines to generate more electricity.

5) <u>Initial costs are often high</u> but there are <u>minimal running costs</u> and it's a <u>reliable</u> energy source.

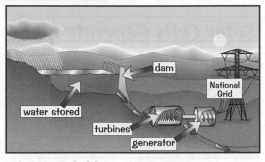

Wave Power — Lots of Little Wave Powered Turbines

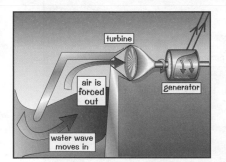

1) Waves can provide an <u>up and down motion</u> which can be used use to drive a <u>generator</u>.

2) Wave power is <u>fairly unreliable</u>, since waves tend to die out when the <u>wind drops</u>.

3) Most electricity generated from wave power uses waves <u>close</u> to the <u>shore</u>. Waves <u>further out</u> in the ocean are much <u>more powerful</u> — <u>offshore wave farms</u> are now being developed to harness this power.

4) Wave power is never likely to provide energy on a <u>large scale</u> but it can be <u>useful</u> on <u>small islands</u>.

Tidal Barrages — Using the Sun and Moon's Gravity

1) <u>Tidal barrages</u> are <u>big dams</u> built across <u>river estuaries</u>, with <u>turbines</u> in them.

2) As the <u>tide comes in</u> it fills up the estuary to a height of <u>several metres</u>. This water can then be allowed out <u>through turbines</u> at a controlled speed. It also drives the turbines on the way in.

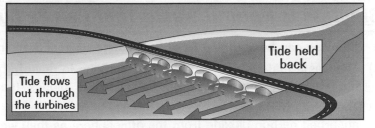

3) Even though it can only be used in a <u>few</u> of the <u>most suitable estuaries</u>, tidal power is a <u>reliable energy source</u> that has the potential to generate a <u>significant amount</u> of energy.

I thought you weren't supposed to mix water and electricity...

Wherever water is <u>moving</u>, you can use it to turn a <u>turbine</u>. The renewable energy sources on this page <u>all</u> involve a flow of <u>water</u> turning a <u>turbine</u>, but they're <u>not</u> the same. Make sure you understand the <u>differences</u> between them and how each one works. Renewable energy is <u>awesome</u> — luckily for you there's a <u>whole</u> other page on it.

Using Renewable Energy Resources

As promised, here's the second page on those lovely, clean, green, renewable energy sources. If it's all getting a bit too much, don't worry — the next page is a bit of a recap to compare all the different energy sources.

Wind Power — Lots of Little Wind Turbines

1) Each wind turbine has its own generator inside it so the electricity is generated directly from the wind turning the blades, which turn the generator.

2) There's no pollution (except for a little bit when they're manufactured).

3) But they do spoil the view and they can be very noisy, which is annoying for people living nearby.

4) They only work when it's windy, so it's not always possible to supply more electricity when there's extra demand.

Solar Cells Generate Electric Currents Directly From Sunlight

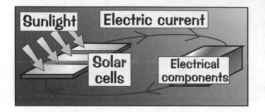

1) Solar cells are usually used to generate electricity on a relatively small scale.

2) Solar power is often used in remote places where there aren't many other ways to generate electricity, and in satellites.

3) In sunny countries solar power is a very reliable source of energy — but only in the daytime. Solar power can still be cost-effective even in cloudy countries like Britain.

Geothermal Energy — Heat from Underground

1) This is only possible in certain places where hot rocks lie quite near to the surface. The source of much of the heat is the slow decay of various radioactive elements, including uranium, deep inside the Earth.

2) Water is pumped in pipes down to the hot rocks and it returns as steam to drive a generator.

3) This is actually brilliant 'free' energy with no real environmental problems.

4) The only big drawbacks are the high setup cost and the fact that there are very few places where this seems to be an economic option (for now).

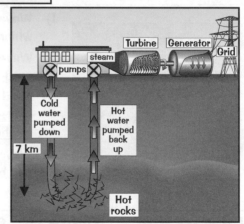

Biomass Is Natural Waste That Can Be Burnt to Produce Electricity

1) Biomass can be anything from farm waste, animal droppings and landfill rubbish to specially grown forests.

2) The waste material is burnt in power stations to drive turbines and produce electricity. Or sometimes it's fermented to produce other fuels such as 'biogas' (usually methane) or ethanol.

3) The plants that grew to produce the waste (or to feed the animals that produced the dung) would have absorbed carbon dioxide from the atmosphere as they were growing. When the waste is burnt this CO_2 is re-released into the atmosphere. So using biomass to generate electricity has no overall effect on atmospheric CO_2 levels — so it's carbon neutral. (Although this only really works if you keep growing plants at the same rate you're burning things.)

The power that you're supplying — it's electrifying...

There's a lot to take in on these two pages but don't panic — it's all pretty straightforward. Make sure you've understood them before you move on to the next one though, as that's about comparing different energy sources.

Comparison of Energy Resources

Setting Up a Power Station

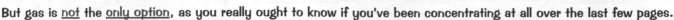

Because coal and oil are running out fast, many old <u>coal- and oil-fired power stations</u> are being <u>taken out of use</u>. Often they're being <u>replaced</u> by <u>gas-fired power stations</u> because these are <u>quick</u> to <u>set up</u>, there's still quite a lot of <u>gas left</u> and gas <u>doesn't pollute as badly</u> as coal and oil.

But gas is <u>not</u> the <u>only option</u>, as you really ought to know if you've been concentrating at all over the last few pages.

When looking at the options for a <u>new power station</u>, there are <u>several factors</u> to consider: How much it <u>costs</u> to set up and run, <u>how long</u> it takes to <u>build</u>, <u>how much power</u> it can generate, etc. Then there are also the trickier factors like <u>damage to the environment</u> and <u>impact on local communities</u>. And because these are often <u>very contentious</u> issues, getting <u>permission</u> to build certain types of power station can be a <u>long-running</u> process, and hence <u>increase</u> the overall <u>set-up time</u>.

Set-Up Costs

<u>Renewable</u> resources often need <u>bigger power stations</u> than non-renewables for the <u>same output</u>. And as you'd expect, the <u>bigger</u> the power station, the <u>more expensive</u>.

<u>Nuclear reactors</u> and <u>hydroelectric dams</u> also need <u>huge</u> amounts of <u>engineering</u> to make them <u>safe</u>, which bumps up the cost.

Reliability Issues

All the <u>non-renewables</u> are <u>reliable energy providers</u> (until they run out).

Many of the <u>renewable</u> sources <u>depend on the weather</u>, which means they're pretty <u>unreliable</u> here in the UK. The <u>exceptions</u> are <u>tidal</u> power and <u>geothermal</u> (which <u>don't</u> depend on weather).

Environmental Issues

If there's a <u>fuel</u> involved, there'll be <u>waste pollution</u> and you'll be <u>using up resources</u>.

If it <u>relies on the weather</u>, it's often got to be in an <u>exposed place</u> where it sticks out like a <u>sore thumb</u>.

Atmospheric Pollution
Coal, Oil, Gas, Biomass
(+ others, though less so)

Visual Pollution
Coal, Oil, Gas, Nuclear, Tidal, Waves, Wind, Hydroelectric, Biomass

Other Problems
Nuclear (dangerous waste, explosions, contamination), Hydroelectric (dams bursting)

Using Up Resources
Coal, Oil, Gas, Nuclear

Noise Pollution
Coal, Oil, Gas, Nuclear, Wind, Biomass

Disruption of Wildlife Habitats
Hydroelectric, Tidal

Set-Up Time

This is affected by the <u>size</u> of the power station, the <u>complexity</u> of the engineering and also the <u>planning issues</u> (e.g. <u>discussions</u> over whether they should be <u>allowed</u> to build a nuclear power station on a stretch of <u>beautiful coastline</u> can last <u>years</u>).

<u>Gas</u> is one of the <u>quickest</u> to set up.

Running/ Fuel Costs

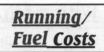

<u>Renewables</u> usually have the <u>lowest running costs</u>, because there's <u>no</u> actual <u>fuel</u> involved (except biomass).

Location Issues

This is fairly <u>common sense</u> — a <u>power station</u> has to be <u>near</u> to the <u>stuff it runs on</u>.

<u>Solar</u> — pretty much <u>anywhere</u>, though the sunnier the better

<u>Gas</u> — pretty much <u>anywhere</u> there's piped gas (most of the UK)

<u>Biomass</u> — pretty much <u>anywhere</u>

<u>Hydroelectric</u> — <u>hilly</u>, <u>rainy</u> places with <u>floodable valleys</u>, e.g. the Lake District, Scottish Highlands

<u>Wind</u> — <u>exposed</u>, <u>windy</u> places like moors and coasts or out at sea

<u>Oil</u> — near the <u>coast</u> (oil transported by sea)

<u>Waves</u> — on the <u>coast</u>

<u>Coal</u> — near <u>coal mines</u>, e.g. Yorkshire, Wales

<u>Nuclear</u> — <u>away from people</u> (in case of disaster), <u>near water</u> (for cooling)

<u>Tidal</u> — big <u>river estuaries</u> where a dam can be built

<u>Geothermal</u> — fairly limited, only in places where <u>hot rocks</u> are <u>near the Earth's surface</u>

Of course — the biggest problem is we demand too much electricity...

It would be lovely if we could get rid of all the <u>nasty polluting power stations</u> and replace them all with clean, green energy, just like that... but it's not quite that simple. Renewable energy has its <u>own problems</u> too, and probably isn't enough to power the <u>whole country</u> without having a wind farm in everyone's back yard.

Electricity and the National Grid

The National Grid is the network of pylons and cables that covers the whole of Britain, getting electricity to homes everywhere. Whoever you pay for your electricity, it's the National Grid that gets it to you.

Electricity Gets Around via the National Grid...

1) The National Grid takes electrical energy from the power stations to just where it's needed in homes and industry.

2) It enables power to be generated anywhere on the grid, and then be supplied anywhere else on the grid.

3) To transmit the huge amount of power needed, you need either a high voltage or a high current (see page 32).

4) The problem with a high current is that you lose loads of energy through heat in the cables.

5) It's much cheaper to boost the voltage up really high (to 400 000 V — eeek!) and keep the current very low.

...With a Little Help from Pylons and Transformers

1) To get the voltage to 400 000 V to transmit power requires transformers as well as big pylons with huge insulators — but it's still cheaper.

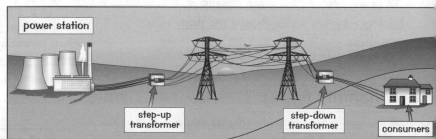

power station

step-up transformer

step-down transformer

consumers

2) The transformers have to step the alternating voltage up at one end, for efficient transmission, and then bring it back down to safe, useable levels at the other end.

3) Transformers all have two coils, the primary and the secondary, joined with an iron core.

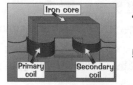

Iron core

Primary coil

Secondary coil

4) The voltage is increased ('stepped up') using a step-up transformer. They have more turns on the secondary coil than the primary coil.

5) It's then reduced again ('stepped down') at the consumer end using a step-down transformer. They have more turns on the primary coil than the secondary.

6) You can calculate the output voltage from a transformer if you know the input voltage and the number of turns on each coil:

$$\frac{\text{Primary Voltage}}{\text{Secondary Voltage}} = \frac{\text{Number of turns on Primary}}{\text{Number of turns on Secondary}}$$

You can use the equation either way up...

$$\frac{V_P}{V_S} = \frac{N_P}{N_S} \quad \text{or} \quad \frac{V_S}{V_P} = \frac{N_S}{N_P}$$

There are Problems with Transmitting Such Huge Amounts of Energy

1) Even at high voltages, electricity transmission isn't very efficient, so power losses are high.

2) The high voltage is a risk to people — e.g. flying a kite into a power line in the rain could be fatal.

3) Some people are worried about the effects on longer-term health of people living near power lines. Links with leukaemia have been suggested, though studies haven't yet found any conclusive evidence.

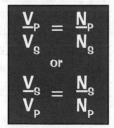

400 000 V — you wouldn't want to fly your kite into that...

If you had your own solar panel or wind generator, you could sell back any surplus electricity to the National Grid. So if you don't use much electricity, but you generate a lot of it, you can actually make money instead of spending it. Nice trick if you can do it. Shame solar panels cost a fortune...

Energy Efficiency & Cost-Efficiency

You Can Save Money by Insulating Your House...

1) If you want to <u>save money</u> on <u>heating bills</u> you can <u>insulate</u> your house — but it costs money to install insulation.

2) Eventually, though, the <u>money you save</u> on your heating bills will <u>equal</u> the <u>initial cost</u> of the insulation — the time this takes is called the <u>payback time</u>. After that you'll save money <u>every year</u>. It's a good idea to work out the payback time <u>before</u> you spend your money, to see if the insulation will be <u>cost-efficient</u>.

3) <u>Cheaper</u> methods of insulation are usually less effective at saving energy — so they save you less money per year. But they often have <u>short payback times</u>, so they're more <u>cost-efficient</u>.

4) If you look at it over, say, a <u>five-year period</u> then a cheap <u>hot water tank jacket</u> wins over expensive <u>double glazing</u>.

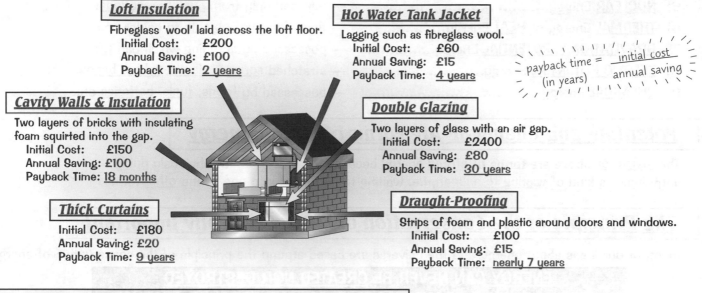

Loft Insulation
Fibreglass 'wool' laid across the loft floor.
Initial Cost: £200
Annual Saving: £100
Payback Time: 2 years

Hot Water Tank Jacket
Lagging such as fibreglass wool.
Initial Cost: £60
Annual Saving: £15
Payback Time: 4 years

Cavity Walls & Insulation
Two layers of bricks with insulating foam squirted into the gap.
Initial Cost: £150
Annual Saving: £100
Payback Time: 18 months

Double Glazing
Two layers of glass with an air gap.
Initial Cost: £2400
Annual Saving: £80
Payback Time: 30 years

Thick Curtains
Initial Cost: £180
Annual Saving: £20
Payback Time: 9 years

Draught-Proofing
Strips of foam and plastic around doors and windows.
Initial Cost: £100
Annual Saving: £15
Payback Time: nearly 7 years

$$\text{payback time (in years)} = \frac{\text{initial cost}}{\text{annual saving}}$$

...and Using More Low-Energy Appliances

<u>Low-energy</u> and <u>efficient</u> appliances will be <u>cheaper to run</u>, but they're often <u>more expensive to buy</u> — you might need to do some <u>maths</u> to work out <u>payback time</u> and <u>cost-efficiency</u>.

EXAMPLE: Maria is choosing a new fridge. Fridge A costs £400 and will save her approximately 19p a day to run compared to her old fridge. Fridge B costs £325 but would only save her 13p a day to run. Which fridge will have the shorter payback time?

ANSWER: Fridge A: annual saving = £0.19 × 365 days = £69.35
Fridge A: payback time = initial cost ÷ annual saving = £400 ÷ £69.35 = <u>5.77 years</u>
Fridge B: annual saving = £0.13 × 365 days = £47.45
Fridge B: payback time = initial cost ÷ annual saving = £325 ÷ £47.45 = <u>6.85 years</u>
5.77 years < 6.85 years, so <u>Fridge A has the shorter payback time</u>.

Energy Can be Measured in Joules or Kilowatt-Hours

1) Energy is normally measured in <u>joules</u> (J) or <u>kilojoules</u> (kJ). 1 kJ = 1000 J.

2) The amount of <u>energy</u> an appliance uses depends on its <u>power</u> and the <u>time</u> you leave it on for. The <u>power</u> of an appliance can be worked out using this equation:

$$\text{POWER (in W)} = \frac{\text{ENERGY (in J)}}{\text{TIME (in s)}}$$

$$\frac{E}{P \times t}$$

3) <u>Electricity meters</u> record how much <u>energy</u> you've used, not in joules, but in "<u>kilowatt-hours</u>" (kWh). A kilowatt-hour is the amount of energy used by a <u>1 kW</u> (1 kW = 1000 W) appliance left on for <u>1 hour</u>.

4) You can work out the <u>cost</u> of using an appliance with the equation on the right. You might have to rearrange it too.

$$\text{COST} = \text{POWER (in kW)} \times \text{TIME (in hours)} \times \text{COST of 1 kWh}$$

Save energy — stay in bed...

When you're dealing with power, time and energy, you normally use the standard units — watts, seconds and joules. When you're talking about the <u>cost</u> of energy, you have to use <u>kilowatts</u>, <u>hours</u> and <u>kWh</u>. <u>Don't forget</u>.

Energy Transfer

Thermal (heat) energy is just one type of energy, but there are lots more as well:

Learn These Nine Types of Energy

You should know all of these <u>well enough</u> by now to list them <u>from memory</u>, including the examples:

1) <u>ELECTRICAL</u> Energy.................................... — whenever a <u>current</u> flows.
2) <u>LIGHT</u> Energy.. — from the <u>Sun</u>, <u>light bulbs</u>, etc.
3) <u>SOUND</u> Energy.. — from <u>loudspeakers</u> or anything <u>noisy</u>.
4) <u>KINETIC</u> Energy, or <u>MOVEMENT</u> Energy...... — anything that's <u>moving</u> has it.
5) <u>NUCLEAR</u> Energy..................................... — released only from <u>nuclear reactions</u>.
6) <u>THERMAL</u> Energy or <u>HEAT</u> Energy............. — <u>flows</u> from <u>hot objects</u> to colder ones.
7) <u>GRAVITATIONAL POTENTIAL</u> Energy.............. — possessed by anything which can <u>fall</u>.
8) <u>ELASTIC POTENTIAL</u> Energy....................... — stretched <u>springs</u>, <u>elastic</u>, <u>rubber bands</u>, etc.
9) <u>CHEMICAL</u> Energy................................... — possessed by <u>foods</u>, <u>fuels</u>, <u>batteries</u> etc.

Potential- and Chemical- Are Forms of Stored Energy

The <u>last three</u> above are forms of <u>stored energy</u> because the energy is not obviously <u>doing</u> anything, it's kind of <u>waiting to happen</u>, i.e. waiting to be turned into one of the <u>other</u> forms.

The Principle of the Conservation of Energy is Really Important

Many of our ideas about energy and the universe are based around the principle of the conservation of energy:

<u>ENERGY</u> CAN NEVER BE <u>CREATED NOR DESTROYED</u>
— IT'S ONLY EVER <u>TRANSFERRED</u> FROM ONE FORM TO ANOTHER.

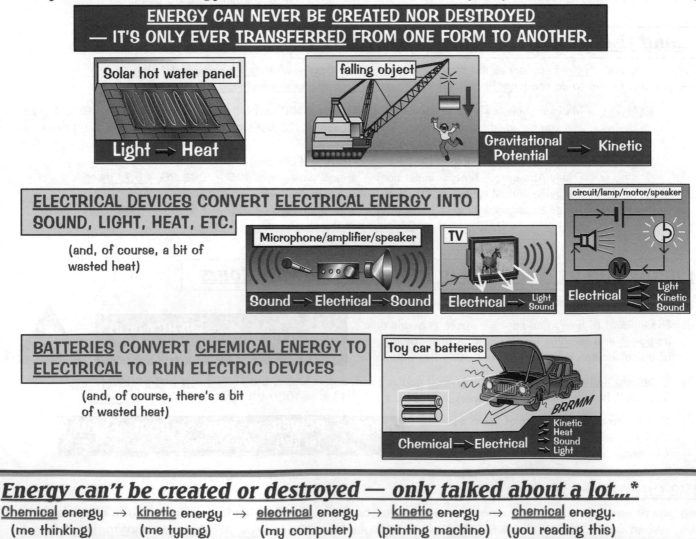

ELECTRICAL DEVICES CONVERT **ELECTRICAL ENERGY** INTO SOUND, LIGHT, HEAT, ETC.

(and, of course, a bit of wasted heat)

BATTERIES CONVERT **CHEMICAL ENERGY** TO **ELECTRICAL** TO RUN ELECTRIC DEVICES

(and, of course, there's a bit of wasted heat)

Energy can't be created or destroyed — only talked about a lot...*

<u>Chemical</u> energy → <u>kinetic</u> energy → <u>electrical</u> energy → <u>kinetic</u> energy → <u>chemical</u> energy.
  (me thinking)   (me typing)   (my computer)   (printing machine)   (you reading this)

* The less well-known "Principle of Conversation of Energy".

Energy Transformations

'Efficiency' is a word that's bandied about a lot in everyday conversations, but in physics it has a specific meaning. Read on and judge for yourself how efficient your revision time has been.

All Machines Waste Some Energy

1) Electrical appliances are just one kind of machine. Machines convert energy from one form to another. Take cars for instance — you put in chemical energy (petrol, diesel or LPG) and the engine converts it into kinetic (movement) energy.

2) The total energy output is always the same as the energy input, but only some of the output energy is useful.

3) This is because some of the input energy is always lost or wasted, often as heat. In a car, some of the chemical energy is converted into heat and sound energy. This is wasted energy — although you could always stick your dinner under the bonnet and warm it up on the drive home.

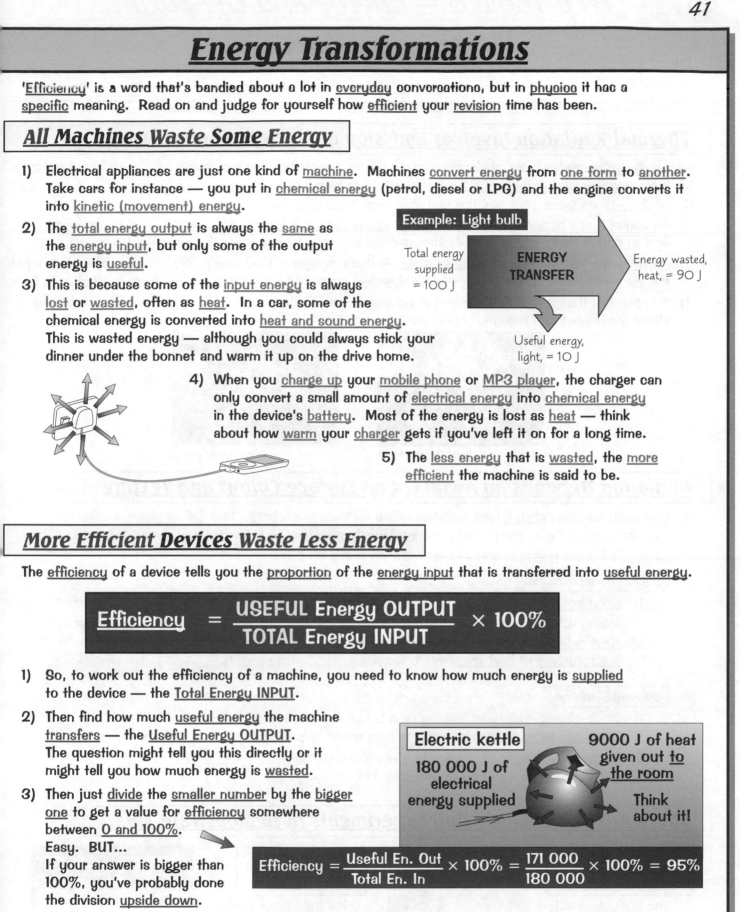

Example: Light bulb

Total energy supplied = 100 J

ENERGY TRANSFER

Energy wasted, heat, = 90 J

Useful energy, light, = 10 J

4) When you charge up your mobile phone or MP3 player, the charger can only convert a small amount of electrical energy into chemical energy in the device's battery. Most of the energy is lost as heat — think about how warm your charger gets if you've left it on for a long time.

5) The less energy that is wasted, the more efficient the machine is said to be.

More Efficient Devices Waste Less Energy

The efficiency of a device tells you the proportion of the energy input that is transferred into useful energy.

$$\text{Efficiency} = \frac{\text{USEFUL Energy OUTPUT}}{\text{TOTAL Energy INPUT}} \times 100\%$$

1) So, to work out the efficiency of a machine, you need to know how much energy is supplied to the device — the Total Energy INPUT.

2) Then find how much useful energy the machine transfers — the Useful Energy OUTPUT. The question might tell you this directly or it might tell you how much energy is wasted.

3) Then just divide the smaller number by the bigger one to get a value for efficiency somewhere between 0 and 100%. Easy. BUT... If your answer is bigger than 100%, you've probably done the division upside down.

Electric kettle

180 000 J of electrical energy supplied

9000 J of heat given out to the room

Think about it!

$$\text{Efficiency} = \frac{\text{Useful En. Out}}{\text{Total En. In}} \times 100\% = \frac{171\,000}{180\,000} \times 100\% = 95\%$$

4) The closer the efficiency is to 100%, the less money you'll waste paying for energy you can't use.

I'm not lazy — I'm just really efficient...

Efficiency is one of those things that'll come up again and again. If I were you, I wouldn't even think about going into the exam without knowing that equation inside out — it's a really important one. It's useful to remember that electric heaters are usually the most efficient machines as all the electricity is converted to "useful" heat.

Heat Radiation

Be careful not to get confused between <u>heat radiation</u> and <u>ionising radiation</u> (see page 20). This page is all about <u>heat energy</u> and the types of <u>materials</u> that are good at <u>absorbing</u> and <u>emitting</u> it.

Thermal Radiation Involves Emission of Electromagnetic Waves

<u>Heat radiation</u> consists purely of electromagnetic waves of a certain range of frequencies — <u>infrared radiation</u>. It's next to visible light in the <u>electromagnetic spectrum</u> (see p.15).

1) <u>All objects</u> are <u>continually</u> emitting and absorbing <u>heat radiation</u>.

2) An object that's <u>hotter</u> than its surroundings <u>emits more radiation</u> than it <u>absorbs</u> (as it <u>cools</u> down). And an object that's <u>cooler</u> than its surroundings <u>absorbs more radiation</u> than it <u>emits</u> (as it <u>warms</u> up).

3) <u>Power</u> is the just the <u>rate of energy change</u> — that's energy ÷ time (see p.39). For an object to stay at the <u>same</u> temperature, the <u>power</u> of heat <u>absorbed</u> needs to be the <u>same</u> as the power <u>emitted</u>.

4) You can <u>feel</u> this <u>heat radiation</u> if you stand near something <u>hot</u> like a fire or if you put your hand just above the bonnet of a recently parked car.

(recently parked car)   (after an hour or so)

Radiation Depends an Awful Lot on Surface Colour and Texture

1) <u>Dark matt</u> surfaces <u>absorb</u> heat radiation falling on them much <u>better</u> than <u>bright glossy</u> surfaces, such as <u>gloss white</u> or <u>silver</u>. They also <u>emit much more</u> heat radiation (at any given temperature).

2) <u>Silvered</u> surfaces <u>reflect</u> nearly all heat radiation falling on them.

<u>Solar hot water panels</u>

1) <u>Solar hot water panels</u> contain <u>water pipes</u> under a <u>black surface</u> (or black painted pipes under glass).

2) <u>Heat radiation</u> from the Sun is <u>absorbed</u> by the <u>black surface</u> to <u>heat the water</u> in the pipes.

<u>Survival Blankets</u>

1) If someone gets injured halfway up a big snowy hill, it can be <u>crucial</u> to <u>keep them</u> as <u>warm</u> as possible till help arrives.

2) A <u>silver coloured blanket</u> helps to <u>stop</u> their body <u>heat radiating away</u> — and could save their life.

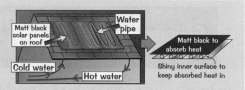

There Are Lots of Fairly Dull Experiments to Demonstrate This...

Here are two of the most gripping:

Leslie's Cube

The <u>matt black</u> side <u>emits most heat</u>, so it's that thermometer which gets <u>hottest</u>.

The Melting Wax Trick

The <u>matt black</u> surface <u>absorbs most heat</u>, so its wax <u>melts</u> first and the ball bearing <u>drops</u>.

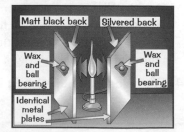

I know it's Leslie's Cube — but he said I could borrow it...

The key idea here is that <u>heat radiation</u> is affected by the <u>colour</u> and <u>texture</u> of surfaces. Thermal radiation questions often ask you <u>why</u> something's painted silver, or how you could <u>reduce the heat losses</u> from something.

Revision Summary for P1b Topics 4, 5 & 6

Well, here we are again. It's time for another round of questions. You've probably had enough of me wittering on by now — so I'll leave you to get stuck in. Good luck, chaps.

1) What is ultrasound? Describe how sonar works.

2) Explain why ultrasound rather than X-rays is used to take images of a foetus.

3) What is infrasound? What are the advantages of using sounds with long wavelengths?

4) Suggest two situations in which scientists might use microphones that are sensitive to infrasound.

5) What are tectonic plates? Why do they move? What can these movements cause?

6) Are predictions of earthquakes based on previous tectonic activity reliable? Why?

7) How do P-waves and S-waves differ regarding: a) type of wave b) speed   c) what they go through?

8) Describe how scientists use information from seismographs to calculate the distance to an earthquake.

9) Why are three (or more) seismometers needed to identify the exact location of an earthquake?

10) Describe the difference between a.c. and d.c..

11)* Draw a diagram of a circuit that you could use to work out the power of a motor.
    What equation would you use to do the calculation?

12) Describe how a voltage can be induced using a magnet and a coil of wire.

13) What is meant by a non-renewable energy resource?
    Name four different non-renewable energy resources.

14) Explain how electricity is generated in a gas-fired power station.

15) State one advantage and two disadvantages of using renewable energy resources.

16) Describe how the following renewable energy resources are used to generate electricity:
    a) waves   b) the tide   c) wind   d) solar energy   e) geothermal energy f) biomass

17) Name six factors that need to be considered when setting up a power station.

18) Explain why a very high voltage is used to transmit electricity in the National Grid.

19)* The following table gives some information about two different light bulbs.
    a) What is the payback time for bulb A?
    b) Which bulb is more cost-efficient?
    c) Bulb A is rated at 0.1 kW. If one unit of electricity costs 8p,
       how much will it cost if the bulb is left on for 5 hours?

	Price of bulb	Annual saving
Bulb A	£2.50	£1.25
Bulb B	£3.00	£2.00

20) Name nine types of energy and give an example of each.

21) Give two examples of forms of stored energy.

22) State the principle of the conservation of energy.

23) The useful energy output of a device is usually much less than the
    total energy input. What happens to the rest of this energy?

24) Write down the formula for calculating efficiency.

25)*What is the efficiency of a motor that converts 100 J
    of electrical energy into 70 J of useful kinetic energy?

26) True or false — an object that's hotter than its surroundings emits more radiation than it absorbs.

27) Explain why solar hot water panels have a matt black surface.

28) Describe an experiment to demonstrate how the colour or texture
    of a material affects the amount of heat energy that it absorbs.

Static Electricity

Static electricity is all about charges which are <u>not</u> free to move. This causes them to build up in one place and it often ends with a <u>spark</u> or a <u>shock</u> when they do finally move. But before we get to all that, we first need to look at the <u>structure</u> of the atom...

Atoms *Have a* Central Nucleus *with* Electrons Moving Round It

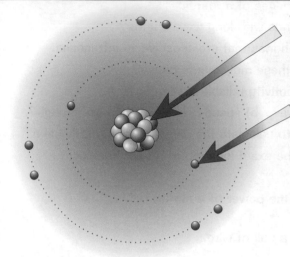

The <u>nucleus</u> is <u>tiny</u> but it makes up most of the <u>mass</u> of the atom. It contains <u>protons</u> (which are <u>positively charged</u>) and <u>neutrons</u> (which are <u>neutral</u>) — which gives it an overall positive charge.

The rest of the atom is mostly <u>empty space</u>. The <u>negative electrons</u> whizz round the outside of the nucleus really fast. They give the atom its <u>overall size</u>. But they have virtually <u>no</u> mass.

Learn the relative charges and masses of each particle:

PARTICLE	MASS	CHARGE
Proton	1	+1
Neutron	1	0
Electron	$\frac{1}{2000}$	-1

Build-up of Static *is Caused by* Friction

1) When two <u>insulating</u> materials are <u>rubbed</u> together, electrons will be <u>scraped off</u> <u>one</u> and <u>dumped</u> on the other.

2) This'll leave a <u>positive</u> static charge on one and a <u>negative</u> static charge on the other.

3) <u>Only</u> electrons can move, <u>not protons</u>. <u>Which way</u> the electrons are transferred <u>depends</u> on the <u>two materials</u> involved.

4) The classic examples are <u>polythene</u> and <u>acetate</u> rods being rubbed with a <u>cloth</u> <u>duster</u>, as shown in the diagrams.

With the <u>polythene rod</u>, electrons move <u>from the duster</u> to the rod. The <u>rod</u> becomes <u>negatively charged</u> and the <u>duster</u> is left with an <u>equal positive charge</u>.

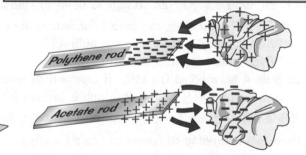

With the <u>acetate rod</u>, electrons move <u>from the rod</u> to the duster. The <u>duster</u> becomes <u>negatively charged</u> and the <u>rod</u> is left with an <u>equal positive charge</u>.

Like Charges Repel, Unlike Charges Attract

This is <u>easy</u> and, I'd have thought, <u>kind of obvious</u>.
Two things with <u>opposite</u> electric charges are <u>attracted</u> to each other.
Two things with the <u>same</u> electric charge will <u>repel</u> each other.
These forces get <u>weaker</u> the <u>further apart</u> the two things are.

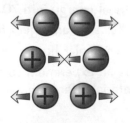

Static caravans — where electrons go on holiday...

<u>Bad hair days</u> are caused by static — it builds up on your hair, so your strands of hair repel each other. Boo static electricity. But before I start a revolution against it, let's have a recap... Insulators can be charged by friction, through the transfer of electrons — leaving one material negatively charged and t'other positively charged.

Static Electricity

You might not realise it, but we often experience some common electrostatic phenomena in our everyday lives. It's shocking stuff...

Static Electricity can Cause Little Sparks or Shocks

1) Clothing Crackles

When synthetic clothes are dragged over each other (like in a tumble drier) or over your head, electrons get scraped off, leaving static charges on both parts. That leads to the inevitable — attraction (they stick together) and little sparks as the charges rearrange themselves.

2) Car Shocks

Static charge can also build up between your clothes and a synthetic car seat — the friction between the two causes electrons to be scraped off. Then, when you get out of the car and touch the metal door, the charge flows and it can give you a real 'buzz'. Some cars have conducting strips which hang down behind the car. This gives a safe discharge to earth (p.46).

3) Shocks From Door Handles

If you walk on a nylon carpet wearing shoes with insulating soles, there will be a transfer of electrons from the carpet to you and charge will build up on your body. Then if you touch a metal door handle, the charge flows to the conductor and you get a little shock.

Some Electrically Charged Objects can Attract Other Objects

1) Balloons can Stick to Walls

Rubbing a balloon against your hair or clothes causes electrons to be transferred to the balloon, leaving it with a negative charge. If you then hold it up against a wall it will stick, even though the wall isn't charged. That's because the charges on the surface of the wall can move a little — the negative charges on the balloon repel the negative charges on the surface of the wall. This leaves a positive charge on the surface, which attracts the negatively charged balloon — this attraction holds the balloon on the wall.

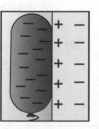

This method of using a charged object to force charges in an uncharged object to move is called induction. And it isn't just balloons and walls where we can see it happen...

2) A Charged Comb can Pick Up Small Pieces of Paper

If you run a comb through your hair, electrons will be transferred to the comb and it will become negatively charged. It can then be used to pick up little pieces of paper, even though they have no charge — holding it near the little pieces of paper causes induction in the paper, which means they stick to the comb.

Lightning is also Caused by a Build-Up of Static Charge

Rain drops and ice bump together inside storm clouds, knocking off electrons and leaving the top of the cloud positively charged and the bottom of the cloud negative. This creates a huge voltage and a big spark.

I know, I know — yet another shocking joke...

Lightning always chooses the easiest path to get to the ground — even if that means going through tall buildings and trees. That's why you should never put up an umbrella or fly a kite in a thunderstorm.

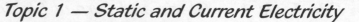

P2a Topic 1 — Static and Current Electricity

Uses and Dangers of Static Electricity

Static electricity can be a bit of a <u>nuisance</u> sometimes, but it also has some <u>good uses</u>, e.g. in industry. But don't get too happy clappy about how wonderful static electricity is — it can be pretty <u>dangerous</u> too.

Paint Sprayers Use Electrostatic Charges to get an Even Coat

1) Bikes and cars are painted using <u>electrostatic paint sprayers</u>.

2) The spray gun is <u>charged</u>, which charges up the small drops of paint. Each paint drop <u>repels</u> all the others, since they've all got the <u>same charge</u>, so you get a very <u>fine spray</u>.

3) The object to be painted is given an <u>opposite charge</u> to the gun. This <u>attracts</u> the fine spray of paint.

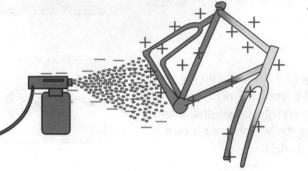

4) This method gives an <u>even coat</u> and hardly any paint is <u>wasted</u>. In addition, parts of the bicycle or car pointing <u>away</u> from the spray gun <u>still receive paint</u>, i.e. there are no paint <u>shadows</u>.

5) Many other electrostatic sprayers work in exactly the <u>same way</u>, e.g. <u>insecticide sprayers</u>.

Just Say No To Electrostatic Sprayers

Electrostatic Charges can Cause a Fuel Filling Nightmare

1) As <u>fuel</u> flows out of a <u>filler pipe</u>, e.g. into an <u>aircraft</u> or <u>tanker</u>, then <u>static can build up</u>.

2) This can easily lead to a <u>spark</u> which might cause an explosion in <u>dusty</u> or <u>fumey</u> places — like when <u>filling up</u> a car with fuel at a <u>petrol station</u>.

3) All these problems with <u>sparks</u> can be solved by <u>earthing charged objects</u> (see below).

fuel tank

Objects Can be Earthed to Stop Electrostatic Charge Building Up

1) Dangerous <u>sparks</u> can be prevented by connecting a charged object to the <u>ground</u> using a <u>conductor</u> (e.g. a copper wire) — this is called <u>earthing</u>.

2) <u>Earthing</u> provides an <u>easy route</u> for the static charges to travel into the ground. This means <u>no charge</u> can <u>build up</u> to give you a shock or make a spark.

3) The <u>electrons</u> flow <u>down</u> the conductor to the ground if the charge is <u>negative</u> and flow <u>up</u> the conductor from the ground if the charge is <u>positive</u>.

4) <u>Fuel tankers</u> must be <u>earthed</u> to prevent any sparks that might cause the fuel to <u>explode</u>.

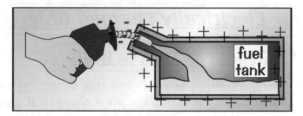

That page really brought me back down to Earth...

As useful as static electricity can be, you've got to be aware of its dangers too. And more importantly how to <u>prevent</u> these dangers. Remember that <u>earthing</u> stops lots of charge building up in once place so there aren't any sparks — which is really important for fuelling aircraft etc. Hmm, let's hope the next page is a bit more cheery.

Charge and Current

This page is all about charges _moving_ in an _electrical circuit_. And if you're worried that reading this might damage your street cred, then let me assure you that it's all _current_. Chortle, chortle.

An Electric Current is the Rate of Flow of Charge

1) Current is the <u>rate of flow of charge</u> around a circuit.

2) In the <u>metal wires</u> of a circuit, this charge is carried by <u>electrons</u>. Metals are <u>good conductors</u> as they have <u>free electrons</u> which are able to move.

3) When <u>current</u> flows past a point in a circuit for a length of <u>time</u> then the <u>charge</u> that has passed is given by this formula:

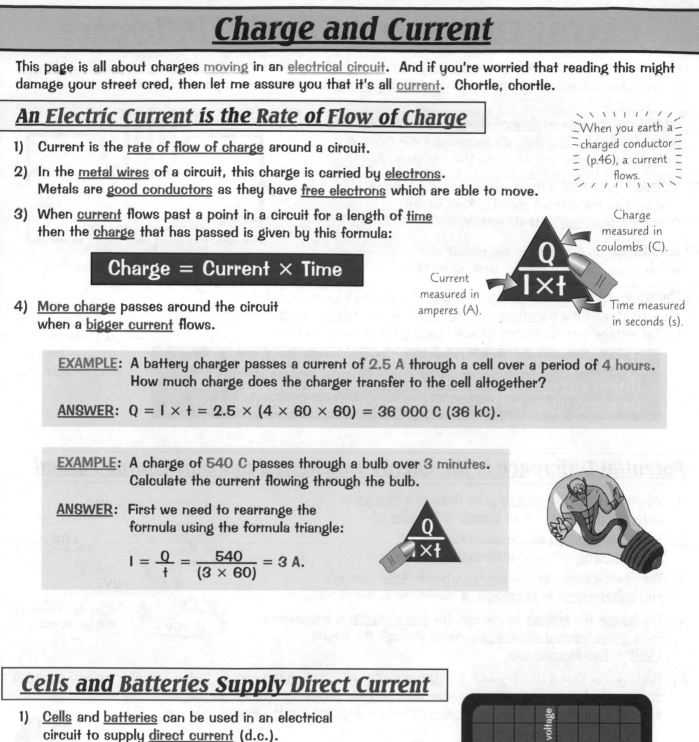

> ### Charge = Current × Time

4) <u>More charge</u> passes around the circuit when a <u>bigger current</u> flows.

When you earth a charged conductor (p.46), a current flows.

Charge measured in coulombs (C).

Current measured in amperes (A).

Time measured in seconds (s).

> **EXAMPLE:** A battery charger passes a current of 2.5 A through a cell over a period of 4 hours. How much charge does the charger transfer to the cell altogether?
>
> **ANSWER:** $Q = I \times t = 2.5 \times (4 \times 60 \times 60) = 36\,000$ C (36 kC).

> **EXAMPLE:** A charge of 540 C passes through a bulb over 3 minutes. Calculate the current flowing through the bulb.
>
> **ANSWER:** First we need to rearrange the formula using the formula triangle:
>
> $$I = \frac{Q}{t} = \frac{540}{(3 \times 60)} = 3 \text{ A}.$$

Cells and Batteries Supply Direct Current

1) <u>Cells</u> and <u>batteries</u> can be used in an electrical circuit to supply <u>direct current</u> (d.c.).

2) Direct current is a current that keeps flowing in the <u>same direction</u>.

3) This means that the <u>charge</u> moves in <u>one direction</u> only.

4) We can look at a direct current trace on an <u>oscilloscope</u>. A direct current source is always at the <u>same voltage</u>, so you get a <u>straight line</u>.

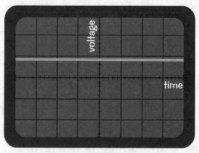

voltage

time

Mains electricity is an <u>alternating</u> current — it is constantly changing direction.

Finding it hard to revise charge and current? Don't QIT it yet...

Formulas, smormulas. They crop up everywhere. Make sure you know how to <u>rearrange</u> and use the one above. Don't forget that the symbol for current is <u>I</u> and the symbol for charge is <u>Q</u>. Barmy. Know all the definitions too, like electric current being the rate of flow of charge. And that direct current only flows in one direction. Good-o.

Electric Current and Potential Difference

Isn't electricity great. Mind you it's pretty bad news if the words don't mean anything to you. Ho hum.
Oh, but what's that? Why it's a shed-load of <u>definitions</u> for you to take a gander at...

1) <u>Current</u> is the rate of <u>flow</u> of charge round the circuit (p.47).
Current will <u>only flow</u> through a component if there is a
<u>voltage</u> across that component. Unit: ampere, A.

2) <u>Voltage</u> (potential difference) is the <u>driving force</u>
that pushes the current round.   Kind of like
"<u>electrical pressure</u>". Unit: volt, V.

3) <u>Resistance</u> is anything in the circuit
which <u>slows the flow down</u>. Unit: ohm, Ω.

4) <u>There's a balance:</u> the <u>voltage</u> is trying to <u>push</u> the current round
the circuit, and the <u>resistance</u> is <u>opposing</u> it — the <u>relative sizes</u>
of the voltage and resistance decide <u>how big</u> the current will be:

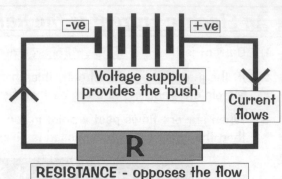

Voltage supply provides the 'push'

Current flows

R

RESISTANCE - opposes the flow

> If you <u>increase the voltage</u> — then <u>more current</u> will flow.
> If you <u>increase the resistance</u> — then <u>less current</u> will flow
> (or <u>more voltage</u> will be needed to keep the <u>same current</u> flowing).

*Potential difference is
just another name for
<u>voltage</u> — they both
mean the <u>same thing</u>.*

Potential Difference is the Energy Transferred per Unit Charge Passed

1) When an electrical <u>charge</u> goes through a <u>change</u> in
<u>potential difference</u>, then <u>energy</u> is <u>transferred</u>.

2) Energy is <u>supplied</u> to the charge at the
<u>power source</u> to 'raise' it through a voltage.

3) The charge <u>gives up</u> this energy when it '<u>falls</u>' through
any <u>voltage drop</u> in <u>components</u> elsewhere in the circuit.

4) The <u>bigger</u> the <u>change</u> in voltage, the <u>more energy</u> is transferred
for a <u>given amount of charge</u> passing through the circuit.
<u>1 volt = 1 joule/coulomb</u>.

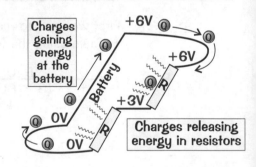

Charges gaining energy at the battery

Charges releasing energy in resistors

5) That means that a battery with a <u>bigger voltage</u> will supply <u>more energy</u> to the circuit for every <u>coulomb</u> of
charge which flows round it, because the charge is raised up "<u>higher</u>" at the start (see above diagram) —
and as the diagram shows, <u>more energy</u> will be <u>dissipated</u> in the circuit too.

Current is Conserved at a Junction

1) In a <u>parallel circuit</u>, each <u>component</u> is <u>separately</u>
connected to the +ve and –ve of the <u>supply</u>.

2) There are <u>junctions</u> where the
current either <u>splits</u> or <u>rejoins</u>.

3) Current <u>doesn't</u> get <u>used up</u> or <u>lost</u> in a circuit —
it is <u>conserved</u>. So, current at a <u>junction</u> is conserved.

4) The total current <u>entering</u> a <u>junction</u> is <u>equal</u>
to the <u>total current leaving</u> a junction.

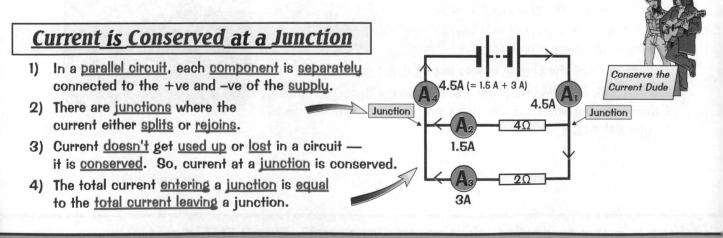

4.5A (= 1.5 A + 3 A)

A₄   Junction   4.5A   A₁   Junction

A₂   4Ω
1.5A

A₃   2Ω
3A

Conserve the Current Dude

I'm always conserved at road junctions...

...which means I'm often late for work. Maybe I should just take the bus. It's really important that you get the
definitions for <u>potential difference</u> and <u>current</u> clear in your head. They pop up lots on the next couple of pages.

Resistance and V = I × R

Ooh oxporimonto, you've gotta love 'em. Here's a <u>simple experiment</u> for investigating resistance.

The Standard Test Circuit

This is without doubt the most totally bog-standard circuit the world has ever known. So know it.

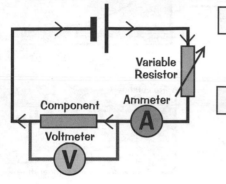

The Ammeter

1) Measures the <u>current</u> (in <u>amps</u>) flowing through the component.
2) Must be placed <u>in series</u> (connected in a line with the component).

The Voltmeter

1) Measures the <u>voltage</u> or <u>potential difference</u> (in <u>volts</u>) across the component.
2) Must be placed <u>in parallel</u> around the <u>component</u> under test — <u>**NOT**</u> around the variable resistor or the cell.

Investigating the Relationship Between Voltage, Current and Resistance

1) The circuit above is a <u>very basic</u> circuit used for testing <u>components</u>, and for getting <u>voltage-current graphs</u> (V-I graphs) for them (see below).
2) The <u>component</u>, the <u>ammeter</u> and the <u>variable resistor</u> are all in <u>series</u>, which means they can be put in <u>any order</u> in the main circuit. The <u>voltmeter</u>, on the other hand, can only be placed <u>in parallel</u> around the <u>component under test</u>, as shown. Anywhere else is a definite <u>no-no</u>.
3) As you <u>vary</u> the <u>variable resistor</u> it alters the <u>current</u> flowing through the circuit (see p.48).
4) This allows you to take several <u>pairs of readings</u> from the <u>ammeter</u> and <u>voltmeter</u>.
5) You can then <u>plot</u> these values for <u>current</u> and <u>voltage</u> on a <u>V-I graph</u>.

Three Hideously Important Voltage-Current Graphs to Learn

V-I graphs show how the current varies as you change the voltage. Learn these three real well:

Fixed Resistors

The current through a <u>resistor</u> (at constant temperature) is <u>proportional to voltage</u>. <u>Different resistors</u> have different <u>resistances</u>, hence the different <u>slopes</u>.

Filament Lamp

As the <u>temperature</u> of the filament <u>increases</u>, the <u>resistance</u> <u>increases</u>, hence the <u>curve</u>.

Diode

Current will only flow through a diode <u>in one direction</u>, as shown.

There's a Formula Linking V and I

You need to know how to use this formula and how to <u>rearrange</u> it:

$$\text{Potential Difference} = \text{Current} \times \text{Resistance}$$

<u>EXAMPLE:</u> A 4 Ω resistor in a circuit has a potential difference of 6 V across it. What is the current through the resistor?

<u>ANSWER:</u> Use the formula V = I × R. We need to find I, so the version we need is I = V/R.

The answer is then: 6/4 which is 1.5 A.

You can use this formula to work out the resistance from a V-I graph, by taking a pair of values (V, I) from the graph and sticking them in the formula R = V/I.

Measure gymnastics — use a vaultmeter...

Learn the experiment above and know what an ammeter and voltmeter are used for, and where they go in a circuit. Remember the shapes of the three example <u>voltage-current graphs</u> too — the examiners love them.

50

Devices and Resistance

Resistors come in all shapes and sizes. Some have fixed resistance, while others can <u>change</u> their resistance...

Light-Dependent Resistor or "LDR" to You

A <u>light-dependent resistor</u> or <u>LDR</u> is a special type of resistor that <u>changes</u> its resistance depending on how much <u>light</u> there is:

1) In <u>bright light</u>, the resistance <u>falls</u>.
2) In <u>darkness</u>, the resistance is <u>highest</u>.

LDR — graph: Resistance in Ω vs Light Intensity (Dark to Light)

Thermistor (Temperature-Dependent Resistor)

A <u>thermistor</u> is like an LDR — but its resistance depends on <u>temperature</u>.

1) In <u>hot</u> conditions, the resistance <u>drops</u>.
2) In <u>cool</u> conditions, the resistance goes <u>up</u>.

Thermistor — graph: Resistance in Ω vs Temperature (Cool to Hot)

Resistors Get Hot When an Electric Current Passes Through Them

1) When there is an <u>electric current</u> in a <u>resistor</u> there is an <u>energy transfer</u> which heats the resistor.

2) This energy transfer is due to the <u>electrons</u> colliding with <u>ions</u> in the <u>lattice</u> that make up the resistor as they move through it.

> A lattice is just the way the ions are arranged.

3) These collisions give the <u>ions</u> in the lattice <u>extra energy</u>, which is emitted as <u>heat</u>. This <u>heating effect</u> increases the resistor's <u>resistance</u> — so <u>less current</u> will flow, or a <u>greater voltage</u> will be needed to produce the same current. If it gets <u>too hot</u>, <u>no current</u> will flow.

4) This heating effect can make electrical circuits <u>less efficient</u>, as some energy is <u>wasted</u> as <u>heat</u>. It can also cause <u>components</u> in the circuit to <u>melt</u> — which means the circuit will <u>stop</u> working, or <u>not work properly</u>. <u>Fuses</u> use this effect to <u>protect</u> circuits — they <u>melt</u> and <u>break</u> the circuit if the current gets <u>too high</u>.

5) The <u>heating effect</u> of an electric current can have other <u>advantages</u>. For example, it's ace if you want to <u>heat</u> something. <u>Toasters</u> contain a coil of wire with a really <u>high</u> resistance. When a current passes through the coil, its <u>temperature increases</u> so much that it <u>glows</u> and gives off infrared (heat) radiation which <u>cooks</u> the bread. <u>Light bulbs</u> work in a similar way.

Electrical Power is the Rate at Which an Appliance Transfers Energy

1) An appliance with a <u>high power rating</u> transfers a <u>lot</u> of <u>energy</u> in a <u>short time</u>.

2) This energy comes from the <u>current</u> flowing through it. This means that an appliance with a <u>high power rating</u> will draw a <u>large current</u> from the supply.

3) Power is measured in <u>watts</u> (W). The formula for <u>electrical power</u> is:

ELECTRICAL POWER = POTENTIAL DIFFERENCE × CURRENT

4) The <u>energy transferred</u> by an appliance depends on the <u>current</u> through it, the <u>voltage</u> supplied to it and <u>how long</u> it is on for (measured in seconds, s). The formula for energy transferred is:

ENERGY TRANSFERRED = CURRENT × POTENTIAL DIFFERENCE × TIME

<u>EXAMPLE</u>: The motor in an electric toothbrush is attached to a <u>3 V</u> battery. If a current of <u>0.8 A</u> flows through the motor for <u>3 minutes</u>, calculate the energy transferred by the motor.

<u>ANSWER</u>: Use E = I × V × t = 0.8 × 3 × (3 × 60) = <u>432 J</u>

Current = heat — so eat fruit cake when you're cold...

Crikey, that page was full to the brim with facts. Make sure you can explain why there is a <u>heating effect</u> when an electric current goes through a resistor. Know how to use those two formulas at the bottom too. Good stuff.

P2a Topic 2 — Controlling and Using Electric Current

Velocity and Acceleration

Speed, velocity, acceleration... no doubt you've heard these words being bandied about during dinner parties. If you've ever felt out of your depth when talk turns to the <u>difference</u> between speed and velocity, then this is the page for you...

Speed and Velocity are Both: *HOW FAST YOU'RE GOING*

Speed and velocity are both measured in <u>m/s</u> (or km/h or mph). They both simply say <u>how fast</u> you're going, but there's <u>a subtle difference</u> between them which <u>you need to know</u>:

> <u>SPEED</u> is just <u>how fast</u> you're going (e.g. 30 mph or 20 m/s) with no regard to the direction.
>
> <u>VELOCITY</u> however must <u>also</u> have the <u>DIRECTION</u> specified, e.g. 30 mph north or 20 m/s, 060°. The distance in a particular direction is called the <u>DISPLACEMENT</u>.

Velocity and displacement are <u>vector quantities</u> — they have magnitude (size) <u>and</u> direction.

Speed, Distance and Time — the Formula:

You really ought to get <u>pretty slick</u> with this <u>very easy equation</u>, it pops up a lot...

$$\text{Speed} = \frac{\text{Distance}}{\text{Time}}$$

<u>EXAMPLE</u>: A cat skulks 20 m in 35 s. Find: a) its speed, b) how long it takes to skulk 75 m.
<u>ANSWER</u>: Using the formula triangle: a) s = d/t = 20/35 = <u>0.57 m/s</u>
                                         b) t = d/s = 75/0.57 = 132 s = <u>2 min 12 s</u>

A lot of the time we tend to use the words "speed" and "velocity" interchangeably. But if you're asked to calculate a velocity in the exam, don't forget to state a <u>direction</u>.

Acceleration is How Quickly Velocity is Changing

Acceleration is <u>definitely not</u> the same as <u>velocity</u> or <u>speed</u>.
1) Acceleration is <u>how quickly</u> the velocity is <u>changing</u>.
2) This change in velocity can be a <u>CHANGE IN SPEED</u> or a <u>CHANGE IN DIRECTION</u> or both.
   (You only have to worry about the change in speed bit for calculations.)

BUT, acceleration is a <u>vector quantity</u> like velocity — it has <u>magnitude</u> and <u>direction</u>.

Acceleration — The Formula:

$$\text{Acceleration} = \frac{\text{Change in Velocity}}{\text{Time taken}}$$

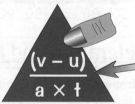

Here, u is the <u>initial velocity</u> of the object and v is its <u>final velocity</u>.

There are <u>two tricky things</u> with this equation. First there's the '(v – u)', which means working out the '<u>change in velocity</u>', as shown in the example below, rather than just putting a <u>simple value</u> for velocity or speed. Secondly there's the <u>unit</u> of acceleration, which is <u>m/s²</u>. (Don't get confused with the units for <u>velocity</u>, m/s).

<u>EXAMPLE</u>: A skulking cat accelerates from 2 m/s to 6 m/s in 5.6 s. Find its acceleration.
<u>ANSWER</u>: Using the formula triangle: a = (v – u) / t = (6 – 2) / 5.6 = 4 ÷ 5.6 = <u>0.71 m/s²</u>

They say a change in velocity is as good as a rest...

Lots of facts to remember there, but it's all important stuff. Make sure you've learnt it all before you move on. Remember — displacement, velocity and acceleration are all <u>vector quantities</u> because they have <u>size</u> and <u>direction</u>.

D-T and V-T Graphs

Make sure you learn all these details real good. Make sure you can <u>distinguish</u> between the two graphs too.

Distance-Time Graphs

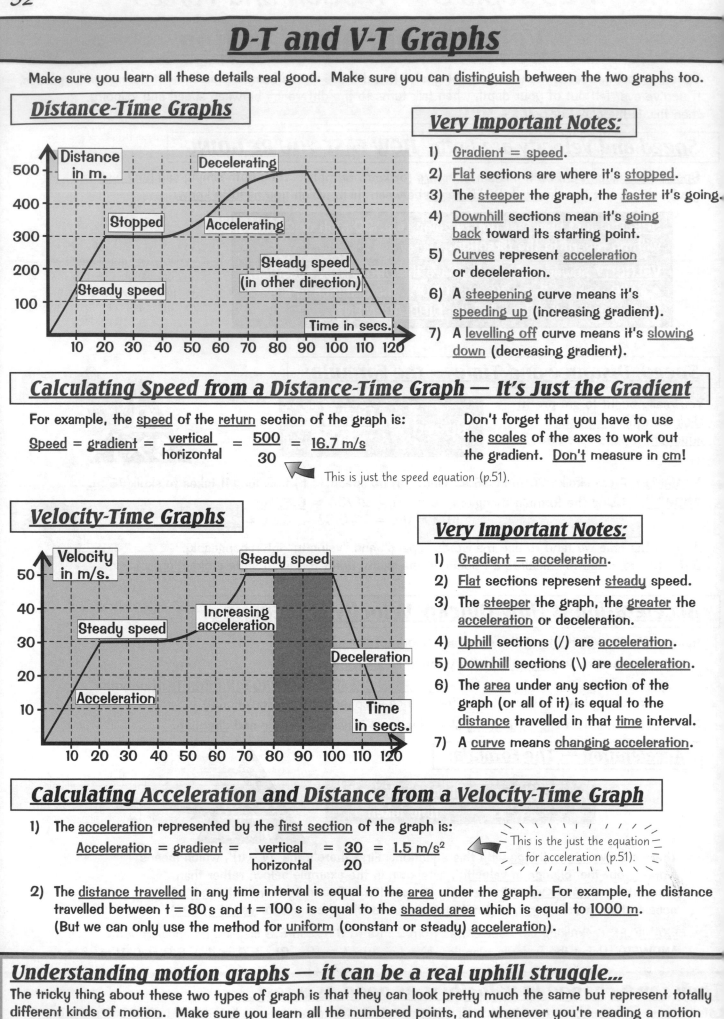

Very Important Notes:

1) <u>Gradient</u> = <u>speed</u>.

2) <u>Flat</u> sections are where it's <u>stopped</u>.

3) The <u>steeper</u> the graph, the <u>faster</u> it's going.

4) <u>Downhill</u> sections mean it's <u>going back</u> toward its starting point.

5) <u>Curves</u> represent <u>acceleration</u> or deceleration.

6) A <u>steepening</u> curve means it's <u>speeding up</u> (increasing gradient).

7) A <u>levelling off</u> curve means it's <u>slowing down</u> (decreasing gradient).

Calculating Speed from a Distance-Time Graph — It's Just the Gradient

For example, the <u>speed</u> of the <u>return</u> section of the graph is:

<u>Speed</u> = <u>gradient</u> = $\dfrac{\text{vertical}}{\text{horizontal}}$ = $\dfrac{500}{30}$ = <u>16.7 m/s</u>

This is just the speed equation (p.51).

Don't forget that you have to use the <u>scales</u> of the axes to work out the gradient. <u>Don't</u> measure in <u>cm</u>!

Velocity-Time Graphs

Very Important Notes:

1) <u>Gradient</u> = <u>acceleration</u>.

2) <u>Flat</u> sections represent <u>steady</u> speed.

3) The <u>steeper</u> the graph, the <u>greater</u> the <u>acceleration</u> or deceleration.

4) <u>Uphill</u> sections (/) are <u>acceleration</u>.

5) <u>Downhill</u> sections (\) are <u>deceleration</u>.

6) The <u>area</u> under any section of the graph (or all of it) is equal to the <u>distance</u> travelled in that <u>time</u> interval.

7) A <u>curve</u> means <u>changing acceleration</u>.

Calculating Acceleration and Distance from a Velocity-Time Graph

1) The <u>acceleration</u> represented by the <u>first section</u> of the graph is:

<u>Acceleration</u> = <u>gradient</u> = $\dfrac{\text{vertical}}{\text{horizontal}}$ = $\dfrac{30}{20}$ = <u>1.5 m/s²</u>

This is the just the equation for acceleration (p.51).

2) The <u>distance travelled</u> in any time interval is equal to the <u>area</u> under the graph. For example, the distance travelled between t = 80 s and t = 100 s is equal to the <u>shaded area</u> which is equal to <u>1000 m</u>. (But we can only use the method for <u>uniform</u> (constant or steady) <u>acceleration</u>).

Understanding motion graphs — it can be a real uphill struggle...

The tricky thing about these two types of graph is that they can look pretty much the same but represent totally different kinds of motion. Make sure you learn all the numbered points, and whenever you're reading a motion graph, <u>check the axis</u> labels carefully so you know which type of graph it is.

Forces

A force is simply a push or a pull. We can draw force diagrams to show the forces acting on an object.

Arrows Show the Size and Direction of Forces

In the exam, you might be given a diagram of an object and asked to draw arrows to show the forces acting on it, or be asked to interpret a force diagram. The three important things to remember are:

1) The length of the arrow shows the size of the force.
2) The direction of the arrow shows the direction of the force (didn't see that one coming, did you...).
3) If the arrows come in opposite pairs, and they're all the same size, then the forces are balanced.

And there are basically only five different force diagrams:

1) Stationary Object — All Forces in Balance

1) The force of GRAVITY (or weight) is acting downwards (see p.54).
2) This causes a REACTION FORCE from the surface pushing the object back up. This is the only way it can be in BALANCE.
3) On the diagram, this is shown by the length of the reaction and weight arrows being the same size and in opposite directions.
4) Without a reaction force, the object would accelerate downwards due to the pull of gravity.
5) The two HORIZONTAL forces must be equal and opposite (or zero) otherwise the object will accelerate sideways. This is shown on the diagram by the two arrows being equal in length and in opposite directions.

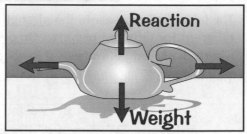

2) Steady Horizontal Velocity — All Forces in Balance

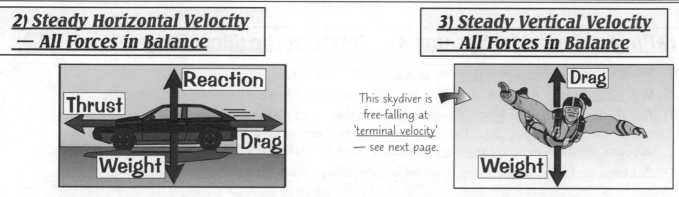

3) Steady Vertical Velocity — All Forces in Balance

This skydiver is free-falling at 'terminal velocity' — see next page.

Take note — to move with a steady speed the forces must be in balance (notice the length and direction of the arrows). If there is an unbalanced force then you get acceleration, not steady speed (see below).

4) Horizontal Acceleration — Unbalanced Forces

1) You only get acceleration with an overall resultant (unbalanced) force — this is shown on the diagrams by the length of one arrow being longer than the arrow in the opposite direction.

2) The bigger this unbalanced force, the greater the acceleration (see p.56).

Note that the forces in the other (perpendicular) direction are still balanced.

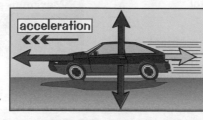

5) Vertical Acceleration — Unbalanced Forces

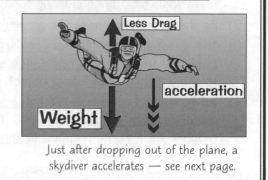

Just after dropping out of the plane, a skydiver accelerates — see next page.

thought skydiving was cool — but it's all about forces...

o, things only accelerate in a particular direction if there's an overall force in that direction. Simple.

Weight and Terminal Velocity

On the last page, we looked <u>forces</u> acting on objects. Here's a bit more on one of those forces — <u>weight</u>.

Weight and Mass are Not the Same

1) <u>Weight</u> is a <u>force</u> measured in <u>newtons</u> (N). Weight is caused by the <u>pull</u> of gravity.

2) <u>Mass</u> is <u>not</u> a force. It is just the <u>amount of 'stuff'</u> in an object. For any given object this will have the same value <u>anywhere</u> in the Universe. Mass is measured in <u>kilograms</u>.

3) An object has the <u>same</u> mass whether it's on <u>Earth</u> or on the <u>Moon</u> — but its <u>weight</u> will be <u>different</u>.

The Very Important Formula Relating Mass, Weight and Gravity

> Weight = mass × gravitational field strength

The letter "g" represents the <u>strength</u> of the gravity, and its value is <u>different</u> for <u>different planets</u>. <u>On Earth</u> g ≈ <u>10 N/kg</u>. <u>On the Moon</u>, where the gravity is weaker, g is only about <u>1.6 N/kg</u>.

This formula is <u>hideously easy</u> to use:

> <u>EXAMPLE:</u> What is the weight, in newtons, of a 5 kg mass, both on Earth and on the Moon?
> <u>ANSWER:</u> "W = m × g". On Earth: W = 5 × 10 = <u>50 N</u>   (The weight of the 5 kg mass is 50 N.)
>   On the Moon: W = 5 × 1.6 = <u>8 N</u>   (The weight of the 5 kg mass is 8 N.)

See what I mean. Hideously easy — as long as you've learnt what all the letters mean.

Falling Objects in a Vacuum Accelerate at the Same Rate

1) The <u>accelerating force</u> acting on <u>all falling objects</u> is <u>gravity</u>.

2) In a <u>vacuum</u>, e.g. in space, gravity makes <u>all</u> objects <u>accelerate</u> at exactly the <u>same rate</u>.

3) This means that on the <u>Moon</u>, hammers and feathers dropped simultaneously will hit the ground <u>together</u>. This happens because there is <u>no air</u> in a vacuum, so there is no <u>air resistance</u> to slow down the falling objects.

4) But here on <u>Earth</u>, where there <u>is</u> air resistance, things are a little different...

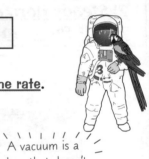

A vacuum is a place that doesn't contain any matter.

Objects Falling Through an Atmosphere Reach a Terminal Velocity

1) On Earth, when falling objects first <u>set off</u> they have <u>much more</u> force (weight) <u>accelerating</u> them than <u>resistance</u> slowing them down.

2) As the <u>speed</u> increases the <u>air resistance</u> increases too.

3) This gradually <u>reduces</u> the <u>acceleration</u> until eventually the <u>air resistance</u> is <u>equal</u> to the <u>weight</u> of the falling object.

4) When these two forces are <u>balanced</u>, the object then <u>won't accelerate</u> any more. It will have reached its maximum speed or <u>terminal velocity</u>.

Velocity

Maximum speed or "terminal velocity"

Time

CGP health and safety tip #49 — beware of falling objects...

That sounded like a threat. It wasn't meant to be. Anyway, remember that all objects falling in a <u>vacuum</u> accelerate at the <u>same rate</u>. But that doesn't happen on Earth because of air resistance. Make sure you know how air resistance affects a falling object, and why it reaches a <u>terminal velocity</u>. Right, I'm off to buy a helmet.

Forces and Motion

The next couple of pages have some really important rules about <u>forces and motion</u>. They were worked out by a chap called Isaac Newton, but you <u>don't</u> need to know about him for the exam. Just this stuff...

When Two Bodies Interact <u>They Exert a Force on Each Other</u>

> If object A <u>exerts a force</u> on object B then object B exerts <u>the exact opposite force</u> on object A.

1) That means if you <u>push</u> something, say a shopping trolley, the trolley will <u>push back</u> against you, <u>just as hard</u>.

2) And as soon as you <u>stop</u> pushing, <u>so does the trolley</u>. Kinda clever really.

3) The force of you pushing the trolley is called the <u>action force</u>. The force of the trolley pushing back against you is called the <u>reaction force</u> (see p.53).

4) So far so good. The slightly tricky thing to get your head round is this — if the forces are always equal, <u>how does anything ever go anywhere</u>? The important thing to remember is that the two forces are acting on <u>different objects</u>. Think about a pair of ice skaters:

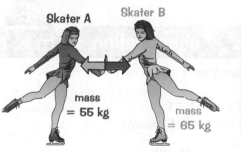

When skater A pushes on skater B (the <u>action</u> force), she feels an equal and opposite force from skater B's hand (the <u>reaction</u> force). Both skaters feel the <u>same sized force</u>, in <u>opposite directions</u>, and so accelerate away from each other. Skater A will be <u>accelerated</u> more than skater B, though, because she has a smaller mass (see p.56).

5) It's the same sort of thing when you go <u>swimming</u>. You <u>push</u> back against the <u>water</u> with your arms and legs, and the water pushes you forwards with an <u>equal-sized force</u> in the <u>opposite direction</u>.

No Resultant Force Means No Change in Velocity

> If there is a <u>zero resultant force</u> acting on a body (the forces are balanced) then the body will <u>remain at rest</u>, or else if it's already moving it'll just carry on at the <u>same velocity</u>.

A resultant force is the overall force acting on a body.

1) When a train or car or bus or anything else is <u>moving</u> at a <u>constant velocity</u> then the <u>forces</u> on it must all be <u>balanced</u> — there is <u>no resultant force</u>.

2) Never let yourself entertain the <u>ridiculous idea</u> that things need a constant overall force to <u>keep</u> them moving — NO NO NO NO NO NO!

3) To keep going at a <u>steady speed</u>, there must be <u>zero resultant force</u> — and don't you forget it.

...have a reaction to forces — they bring me out in a rash...

Ooh the stuff on that page is a bit tricky. Remember, when two objects touch, they exert an <u>equal and opposite</u> force on each other. Know what is meant by <u>action</u> and <u>reaction forces</u> too. And don't forget that if the resultant force on an object is <u>zero</u>, the object will either <u>remain still</u> or keeping going at a <u>constant velocity</u>.

Force and Acceleration

A Resultant Force Means Acceleration

If the resultant force acting on a body is <u>not zero</u>, it will <u>accelerate</u> in the <u>direction</u> of the <u>resultant force</u>.

1) An <u>unbalanced</u> force will always produce <u>acceleration</u> (or deceleration).
2) This "<u>acceleration</u>" can take <u>five</u> different forms:
   <u>starting</u>, <u>stopping</u>, <u>speeding up</u>, <u>slowing down</u> and <u>changing direction</u>.
3) On a force diagram, the <u>arrows</u> will be <u>unequal</u>.
4) <u>Force</u> is a <u>vector quantity</u> — it has <u>magnitude</u> and <u>direction</u> (see p.51).

<u>Don't ever say</u>: "If something's moving there must be an overall resultant force acting on it".
Not so. If there's an <u>overall</u> force it will always <u>accelerate</u>. You get <u>steady</u> speed from <u>balanced</u> forces.

1) The bigger the <u>resultant force</u>, the <u>greater</u> the <u>acceleration</u> or <u>deceleration</u>.
2) The bigger the <u>mass</u> of the object, the <u>smaller the acceleration</u>.
3) To get a <u>big</u> mass to accelerate <u>as fast</u> as a <u>small</u> mass it needs a <u>bigger</u> resultant force.

There is an Equation for Resultant Force

Any <u>resultant force</u> will produce
<u>acceleration</u>, and this is the <u>formula</u> for it:

Force = mass × acceleration

$$\frac{F}{m \times a}$$

<u>EXAMPLE:</u> A car of mass of 1750 kg has an engine which provides a driving force of 5200 N.
At 70 mph the drag force acting on the car is 5150 N.
Find its acceleration a) when first setting off from rest, and b) at 70 mph.

<u>ANSWER:</u> 1) First draw a force diagram for both cases (no need to show the vertical forces):

5200N 0mph   5200N 5150N 70mph

2) Work out the resultant force in each case, and apply "F = ma" using the formula triangle:
   Resultant force = 5200 N   Resultant force = 5200 − 5150 = 50 N
   a = F/m = 5200 ÷ 1750 = <u>3.0 m/s²</u>   a = F/m = 50 ÷ 1750 = <u>0.03 m/s²</u>

You can Investigate F = ma Using a Trolley

To reduce the effects of friction make sure your runway's smooth.

1) Set up your apparatus like the diagram shown on the right.
2) To see how the trolley's <u>acceleration</u> is affected by the <u>force</u> acting on it, keep the <u>mass</u> of the trolley <u>constant</u> and <u>vary</u> the <u>force</u>.
3) <u>Hold</u> the trolley, add <u>100 g</u> mass to the end of the string and then <u>release</u> the trolley. The 100 g mass pulls the trolley with a <u>constant force</u> (<u>F = mg</u>, where g is the <u>acceleration</u> due to <u>gravity</u>).
4) The <u>light gate</u> detects <u>each</u> piece of card as it passes through it and <u>breaks</u> a light beam.
5) <u>Data logging software</u> uses the width of the <u>first</u> piece of card (input into the computer) and the <u>time</u> it blocked the light beam to work out the 'initial' velocity of the trolley (using velocity = distance ÷ time). The same is done with the <u>second</u> piece of card to work out the trolley's 'final' velocity.
6) You can work out the trolley's <u>acceleration</u> using <u>acceleration = (final velocity − initial velocity) ÷ time</u> (see p.51). The <u>time</u> is the time it took for the <u>whole trolley</u> to pass through the light gate.
7) You should <u>repeat</u> the experiment several times and get an <u>average value</u> for the acceleration.
8) Repeat the whole thing again using <u>different masses</u>. You should find the <u>greater</u> the force, the <u>greater</u> the acceleration.
9) You can investigate the relationship between <u>mass</u> and <u>acceleration</u> by varying the <u>trolley's mass</u> and keeping the mass on the string the <u>same</u> (so the force is constant). You should find the <u>greater</u> the <u>mass</u>, the <u>smaller</u> the <u>acceleration</u>.

Card ... *Light gate* ... *Wire to data logger* ... *String* ... *Trolley* ... *Pull* ... *Runway* ... *Masses*

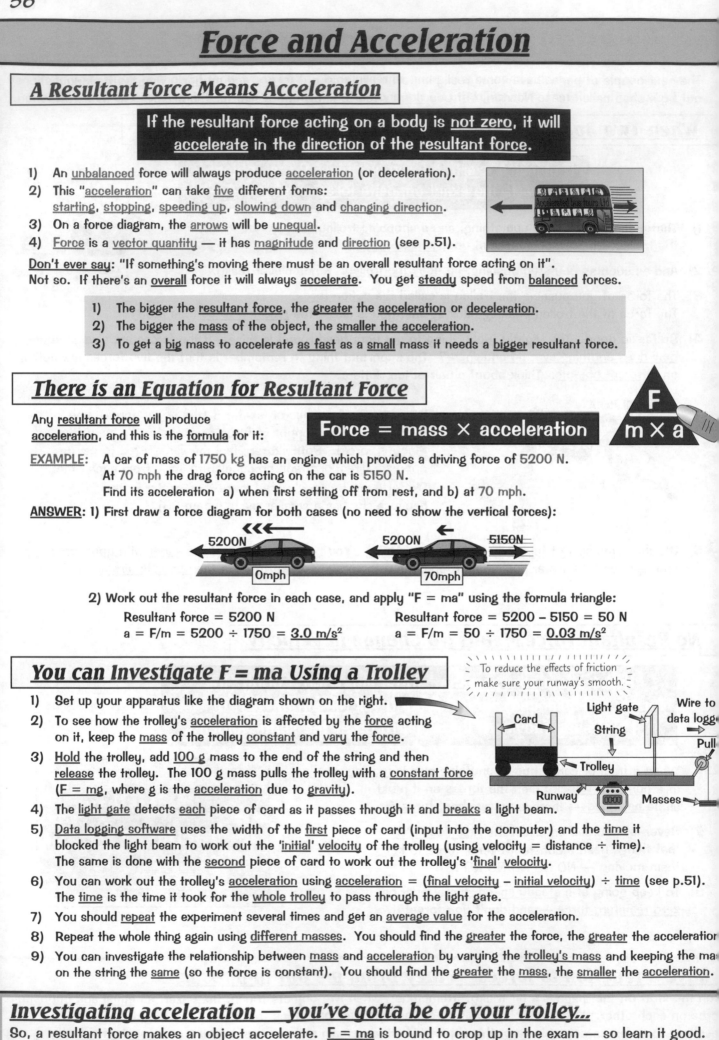

Investigating acceleration — you've gotta be off your trolley...

So, a resultant force makes an object accelerate. <u>F = ma</u> is bound to crop up in the exam — so learn it good.

Revision Summary for P2a Topics 1, 2 & 3

More jolly questions which I know you're going to really enjoy. You know what to do with the tricky questions — read over the relevant stuff again, then have another go at them. Keep at it 'til you can do every question.

1) Draw and label a sketch to show the structure of an atom.
2) Draw a table stating the relative mass and charge of protons, neutrons and electrons.
3) What causes the build-up of static electricity? Which particles move when static builds up?
4) Give three examples of how static electricity can be a nuisance.
5) Explain why a negatively charged comb is able to pick up little pieces of uncharged paper.
6) Describe how electrostatic paint sprayers use static electricity to get an even coat of paint.
7) Explain how you can reduce the danger of getting a static electric shock.
8) Give a definition for current.
9) * A charge of 900 C passes through a component over 10 minutes.
     Calculate the current flowing through the component.
10) What type of current do cells and batteries supply?
11) Explain what voltage and resistance are in an electric circuit. How does the current depend on them?
12) Explain what is meant by potential difference.
13) Sketch typical voltage-current graphs for: a) a fixed resistor, b) a filament lamp, c) a diode.
     Explain the shape of each graph.
14) * Calculate the resistance of a wire if the voltage across it is 12 V and the current through it is 2.5 A.
15) Describe how the resistance of an LDR varies with light intensity.
16) Explain why resistors get hot when an electric current passes through them.
17)* Calculate the current that flows through a toaster rated 230 V, 1100 W.
18) What's the difference between speed and velocity? Give an example of each.
19)* Write down the formula for working out speed. Find the speed of a partly chewed mouse which hobbles
     3.2 m in 35 s. Find how far he would get in 25 minutes.
20)*A speed camera is set up in a 30 mph (13.4 m/s) zone. It takes two photographs 0.5 s apart.
     A car travels 6.3 m between the two photographs. Was the car breaking the speed limit?
21) What is acceleration? What is the unit used?
22)*Write down the formula for acceleration. What's the acceleration of a soggy pea flicked from rest to a
     speed of 14 m/s in 0.4 seconds?
23) Sketch a typical distance-time graph and point out all the important parts of it.
24) Explain how to calculate speed from a distance-time graph.
25) Sketch a typical velocity-time graph and point out all the important parts.
26) Explain how to find velocity, distance and acceleration from a velocity-time graph.
27) Sketch five standard force diagrams, showing the forces and the types of motion.
28) What's the formula for weight? Illustrate it with a worked example of your own.
29) What is "terminal velocity"?
30) Explain what a reaction force is and where it pops up.
31) If an object has zero resultant force on it, can it be moving? Can it be accelerating?
32)*Write down the formula relating resultant force and acceleration.
     A force of 30 N pushes a trolley of mass 4 kg. What will be its acceleration?

Stopping Distances

The stopping distance of a car is the distance covered in the time between the driver <u>first spotting</u> a hazard and the car coming to a <u>complete stop</u>. Examiners are pretty keen on this, so make sure you <u>learn it properly</u>.

Many Factors Affect Your Total Stopping Distance

The distance it takes to stop a car is made up of the <u>sum</u> of the <u>THINKING DISTANCE</u> and the <u>BRAKING DISTANCE</u>.

1) Thinking Distance

"The distance the car travels in the time between the driver noticing the hazard and applying the brakes."

It's affected by <u>TWO MAIN FACTORS</u>:

a) <u>Your REACTION time</u> — this is affected by <u>tiredness</u>, <u>drugs</u>, <u>alcohol</u>, <u>old age</u>, and a <u>careless</u> blasé attitude.

b) <u>How FAST you're going</u> — obviously. Whatever your reaction time, the <u>faster</u> you're going, the <u>further</u> you'll go.

2) Braking Distance

"The distance the car travels during its deceleration whilst the brakes are being applied."

It's affected by <u>FOUR MAIN FACTORS</u>:

a) <u>How FAST you're going</u> — the <u>faster</u> you're going, the <u>further</u> it takes to stop.

b) <u>The MASS of your vehicle</u> — with the <u>same</u> brakes, <u>a heavily laden</u> vehicle takes <u>longer to stop</u>. A car won't stop as quickly when it's full of people and luggage and towing a caravan.

c) <u>How good your BRAKES are</u> — all brakes must be checked and maintained <u>regularly</u>. Worn or faulty brakes will let you down <u>catastrophically</u> just when you need them the <u>most</u>, i.e. in an <u>emergency</u>.

d) <u>How good the GRIP is</u> — you need <u>friction</u> between your <u>tyres</u> and the <u>road surface</u> in order to be able to <u>stop</u>. This depends on:

1) <u>road surface</u>, 2) <u>weather</u> conditions, 3) <u>tyres</u>.

The figures below for typical stopping distances are from the Highway Code. It's frightening to see just how far it takes to stop when you're going at 70 mph.

30 mph	50 mph	70 mph
9 m	15 m	21 m
14 m	38 m	75 m
6 car lengths	13 car lengths	24 car lengths

Thinking distance

Braking distance

Leaves, diesel spills and muck on the road are <u>serious hazards</u> because they're <u>unexpected</u>. <u>Wet</u> or <u>icy roads</u> are always much more <u>slippy</u> than dry roads because there isn't much <u>friction</u> between the tyres and the road. A tyre <u>tread depth</u> of at least <u>1.6 mm</u> is essential for getting rid of the <u>water</u> in wet conditions. Without it, a tyre will simply <u>ride</u> on a <u>layer of water</u> and skid <u>very easily</u>. This is called "<u>aquaplaning</u>" and isn't nearly as cool as it sounds.

The Amount You Slide Depends on Friction

You can investigate how much <u>frictional force</u> different <u>surfaces</u> provide with a simple experiment:

1) Set up your <u>apparatus</u> as shown here:
2) Add <u>masses</u> one by one to the <u>mass holder</u> to provide a <u>force</u> on the block until it eventually <u>slides</u>.
3) The <u>amount</u> of force (the amount of mass) you need to slide the block will depend on the amount of <u>friction</u> between the <u>block</u> and the <u>surface</u>, just like the <u>tyres</u> of a vehicle driving on different <u>road surfaces</u>.
4) You can experiment with different surfaces — try foil, sandpaper, plastic covered in washing up liquid etc.
5) The <u>smaller</u> the frictional force between the block and the surface, the <u>smaller</u> the force you'll need to make the block slide.

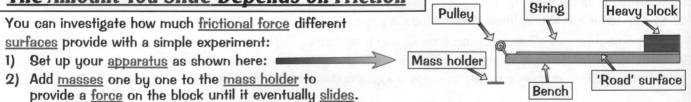

Pulley | String | Heavy block | Mass holder | Bench | 'Road' surface

Stop right there — and learn this page...

Scary stuff. Makes you think doesn't it. Learn all the details and write yourself a <u>mini-essay</u> to see how much you really know. You might have to interpret charts of stopping distance in your exam.

Car Safety

A large lorry being driven very fast is going to be a lot harder to stop than a granny on a bicycle out for a Sunday afternoon ride — that's momentum for you.

Momentum = Mass × Velocity

1) The greater the mass of an object and the greater its velocity, the more momentum the object has.

2) Momentum is a vector quantity — it has size and direction (like velocity, but not speed, see p.51).

$$\frac{momentum}{mass \times velocity}$$

Momentum (kg m/s) = Mass (kg) × Velocity (m/s)

Momentum Before = Momentum After

Momentum is conserved when no external forces act, i.e. the total momentum after is the same as it was before. This is particularly obvious when you have a linear system — when the forces are working along the same line.

Example:

Two skaters approach each other, collide and move off together as shown. At what velocity do they move after the collision?

2 m/s — Ed — 80 kg — Before

1.5 m/s — Sue — 60 kg

Velocity (v) = ? — (80+60) kg — After

1) Choose which direction is positive. I'll say "positive" means "to the right".

2) Total momentum before collision
= momentum of Ed + momentum of Sue
= {80 × 2} + {60 × (−1.5)} = 70 kg m/s

3) Total momentum after collision
= momentum of Ed and Sue together
= 140 × v

4) So 140v = 70, i.e. v = 0.5 m/s to the right.

Forces Cause Changes in Momentum

1) When a force acts on an object, it causes a change in momentum.

2) A larger force means a faster change of momentum (and so a greater acceleration, see p.56).

3) Likewise, if someone's momentum changes very quickly (like in a car crash), the forces on the body will be very large, and more likely to cause injury.

4) This is why cars are designed with protective features to slow people down over a longer time when they have a crash — the longer it takes for a change in momentum, the smaller the force.

$$Force (N) = \frac{Change\ in\ momentum\ (kg\,m/s)}{Time\ (s)}$$

$$F = \frac{mv - mu}{t}$$

Here, 'v' is the final velocity, 'u' is the initial velocity and m is the mass.

| CRUMPLE ZONES crumple on impact, increasing the time taken for the car to stop. | SEAT BELTS stretch slightly, increasing the time taken for the wearer to stop. This reduces the forces acting on the chest. | AIR BAGS also slow you down more gradually. |

5) Bubble wrap works in a similar way to crumple zones as it increases the time over which any knocks and bumps happen to the stuff inside it — so it reduces the forces on your precious bit of kit.

The effect of crumple zones can be shown using eggs. Drop an egg on a hard floor and the force of the impact will shatter it immediately. Drop it onto cushions, surround it in foam or build some more elaborate crumple zone out of cardboard and bubble wrap and you might be more lucky. All because the collision happens over a longer time, and so the force on the egg is smaller.

Learn this stuff — it'll only take a moment... um...

Momentum's a pretty fundamental bit of Physics — so make sure you learn it properly. Bubble wrap is a good demonstration of the relationship between force and momentum — the changes in momentum take longer, reducing the force. Who'd have thought bubble wrap could be so educational... And so darned satisfying to pop.

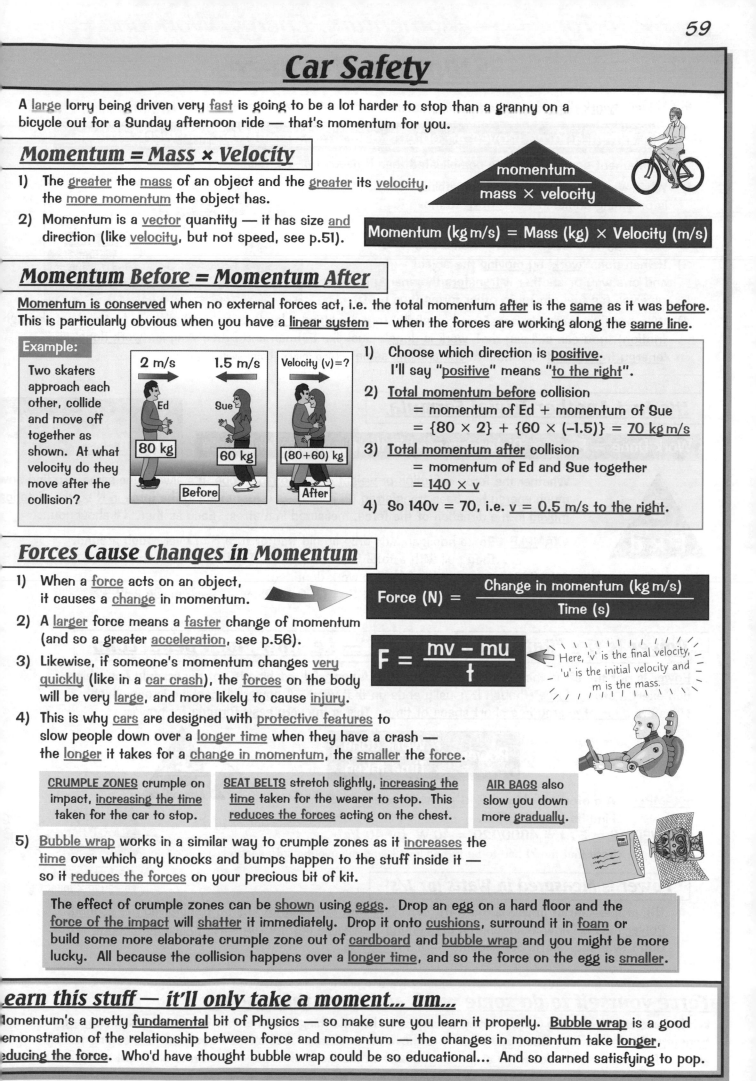

Work and Power

In Physics, "work done" means something special — it's got its own formula and everything.

When a force moves an object, energy is transferred and work is done.

That statement sounds far more complicated than it needs to. Try this:

1) Whenever something moves, something else is providing some sort of 'effort' to move it.

2) The thing putting the effort in needs a supply of energy (like fuel or food or electricity etc.).

3) It then does 'work' by moving the object — and one way or another it transfers the energy it receives (as fuel etc.) into other forms (see p.40).

4) Whether this energy is transferred 'usefully' (e.g. by lifting a load) or is 'wasted' (e.g. lost as heat through friction), you can still say that 'work is done'. Just like Batman and Bruce Wayne, 'work done' and 'energy transferred' are indeed 'one and the same'. (And they're both given in joules.)

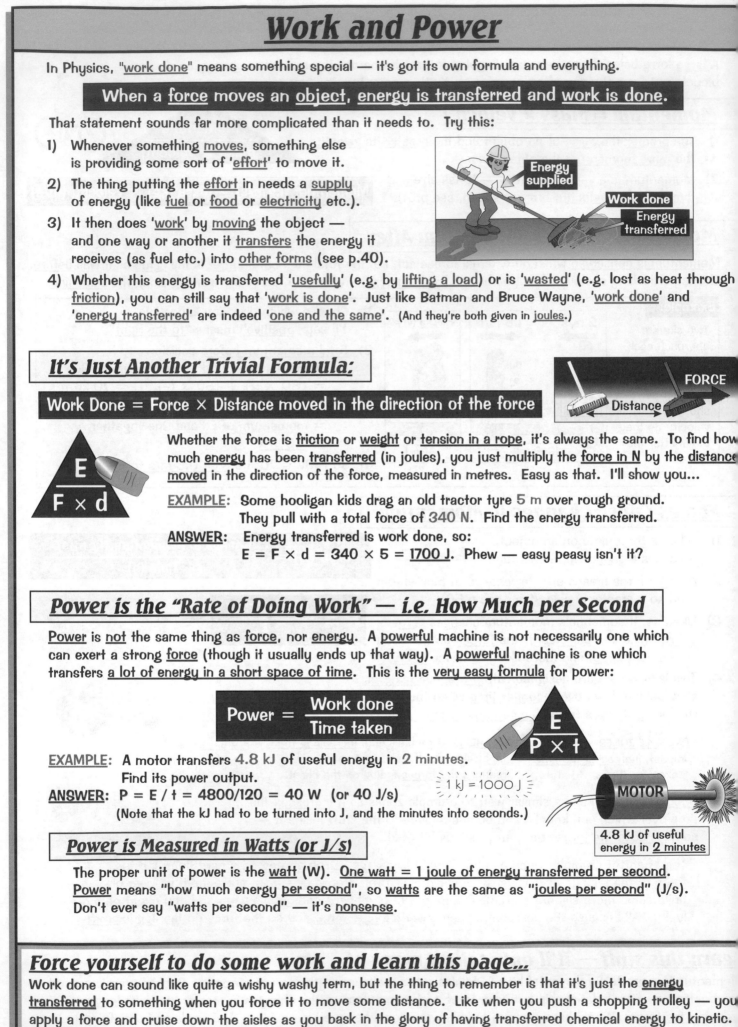

It's Just Another Trivial Formula:

Work Done = Force × Distance moved in the direction of the force

$$\frac{E}{F \times d}$$

Whether the force is friction or weight or tension in a rope, it's always the same. To find how much energy has been transferred (in joules), you just multiply the force in N by the distance moved in the direction of the force, measured in metres. Easy as that. I'll show you...

EXAMPLE: Some hooligan kids drag an old tractor tyre 5 m over rough ground. They pull with a total force of 340 N. Find the energy transferred.

ANSWER: Energy transferred is work done, so:
E = F × d = 340 × 5 = 1700 J. Phew — easy peasy isn't it?

Power is the "Rate of Doing Work" — i.e. How Much per Second

Power is not the same thing as force, nor energy. A powerful machine is not necessarily one which can exert a strong force (though it usually ends up that way). A powerful machine is one which transfers a lot of energy in a short space of time. This is the very easy formula for power:

$$\text{Power} = \frac{\text{Work done}}{\text{Time taken}}$$

$$\frac{E}{P \times t}$$

EXAMPLE: A motor transfers 4.8 kJ of useful energy in 2 minutes. Find its power output.

ANSWER: P = E / t = 4800/120 = 40 W (or 40 J/s)
(Note that the kJ had to be turned into J, and the minutes into seconds.)

1 kJ = 1000 J

4.8 kJ of useful energy in 2 minutes

Power is Measured in Watts (or J/s)

The proper unit of power is the watt (W). One watt = 1 joule of energy transferred per second. Power means "how much energy per second", so watts are the same as "joules per second" (J/s). Don't ever say "watts per second" — it's nonsense.

Force yourself to do some work and learn this page...

Work done can sound like quite a wishy washy term, but the thing to remember is that it's just the energy transferred to something when you force it to move some distance. Like when you push a shopping trolley — you apply a force and cruise down the aisles as you bask in the glory of having transferred chemical energy to kinetic.

Kinetic and Potential Energy

Sat high on your stool in science class you have <u>gravitational potential energy</u> — there's always the potential to fall backwards off it and look a right numpty. So be careful to sit up straight, studying's a dangerous business...

Kinetic Energy is Energy of Movement

Anything that's <u>moving</u> has <u>kinetic energy</u>. There's a slightly <u>tricky formula</u> for it, so you have to concentrate a little bit <u>harder</u> for this one. But hey, that's life — it can be real tough sometimes:

> Kinetic Energy = ½ × mass × velocity²

K.E.
½×m×v²

<u>EXAMPLE</u>: A car of mass 2450 kg is travelling at 38 m/s.
   Calculate its kinetic energy.
<u>ANSWER</u>: Plug the numbers into the formula — but watch the 'v²'!
   K.E. = ½mv² = ½ × 2450 × 38² = <u>1 768 900 J</u>. (<u>Joules</u> because it's <u>energy</u>.)

Remember, the <u>kinetic energy</u> of something depends both on <u>mass</u> and <u>velocity</u>.
The <u>more it weighs</u> and the <u>faster it's going</u>, the <u>bigger</u> its kinetic energy will be.

small mass, not fast
low kinetic energy

big fast
lorries Ltd

big mass, real fast
high kinetic energy

Stopping Distances Increase Alarmingly with Extra Speed

To stop a car, the <u>kinetic energy</u>, ½mv², has to be <u>converted to heat energy</u> at the <u>brakes and tyres</u>:

> Initial Kinetic Energy = Work Done by Brakes to Stop Vehicle
> ½ × m × v² = F × d

v = <u>velocity</u> of car   F = maximum <u>braking force</u>   d = <u>braking distance</u>

<u>Learn this real good</u>: if you <u>double the speed</u>, you double the value of <u>v</u>, but the <u>v²</u> means that the <u>K.E.</u> is then increased by a factor of <u>four</u>. However, 'F' is always the <u>maximum possible</u> braking force which <u>can't</u> be increased, so <u>d</u> must also increase by a factor of <u>four</u> to make the equation <u>balance</u>, i.e. if you go <u>twice as fast</u>, the <u>braking distance</u> 'd' (see p.58) must increase by a <u>factor of four</u> to dissipate the <u>extra K.E.</u>

Gravitational Potential Energy is Energy Due to Height

> Gravitational Potential Energy = mass × g × height

G.P.E.
m×g×h

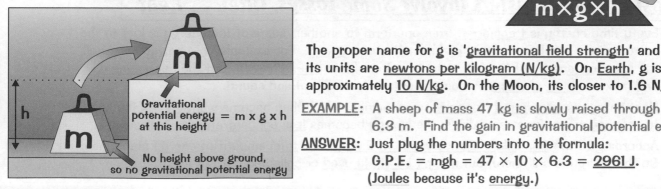

Gravitational
potential energy = m x g x h
at this height

No height above ground,
so no gravitational potential energy

The proper name for g is '<u>gravitational field strength</u>' and its units are <u>newtons per kilogram (N/kg)</u>. On <u>Earth</u>, g is approximately <u>10 N/kg</u>. On the Moon, its closer to 1.6 N/kg.

<u>EXAMPLE</u>: A sheep of mass 47 kg is slowly raised through
   6.3 m. Find the gain in gravitational potential energy.
<u>ANSWER</u>: Just plug the numbers into the formula:
   G.P.E. = mgh = 47 × 10 × 6.3 = <u>2961 J</u>.
   (Joules because it's <u>energy</u>.)

Shopping distance — I can carry on for miles...

The stopping distance of a vehicle depends on the <u>initial velocity squared</u>. And the 'squared' makes all the difference — if you're going three times as fast, it will take you nine times as long to stop. A good reason to drive safely then.

Conservation of Energy

What goes up must come down — that's the principle of the <u>conservation of energy</u> in action. It's a really fundamental concept behind pretty much everything in physics. A good one to get your head around then.

The Principle of the Conservation of Energy Can be Stated Thus:

You've met this before in Physics 1b (page 40), but you need it for this module too. So learn it now:

> **Energy can never be <u>created nor destroyed</u>**
> **— only <u>transferred</u> from one form to another.**

Another <u>important principle</u> which you need to <u>learn</u> is this one:

> **Energy is <u>only useful</u> when it's <u>transferred</u> from one form to another.**

Calculating the Speed of Falling Objects

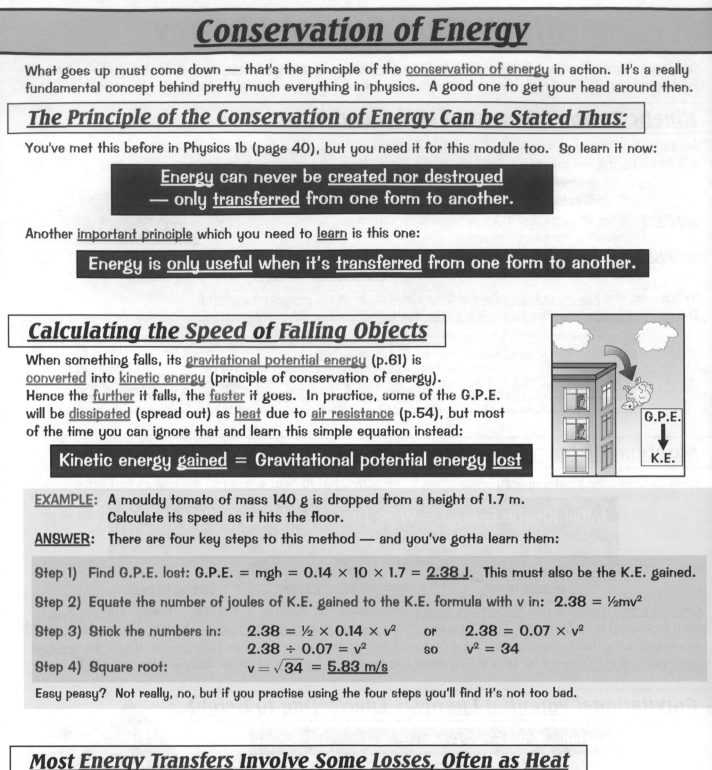

When something falls, its <u>gravitational potential energy</u> (p.61) is <u>converted</u> into <u>kinetic energy</u> (principle of conservation of energy). Hence the <u>further</u> it falls, the <u>faster</u> it goes. In practice, some of the G.P.E. will be <u>dissipated</u> (spread out) as <u>heat</u> due to <u>air resistance</u> (p.54), but most of the time you can ignore that and learn this simple equation instead:

> **Kinetic energy <u>gained</u> = Gravitational potential energy <u>lost</u>**

G.P.E.
↓
K.E.

EXAMPLE: A mouldy tomato of mass 140 g is dropped from a height of 1.7 m. Calculate its speed as it hits the floor.

ANSWER: There are four key steps to this method — and you've gotta learn them:

Step 1) Find G.P.E. lost: G.P.E. = mgh = 0.14 × 10 × 1.7 = <u>2.38 J</u>. This must also be the K.E. gained.

Step 2) Equate the number of joules of K.E. gained to the K.E. formula with v in: $2.38 = \frac{1}{2}mv^2$

Step 3) Stick the numbers in: $2.38 = \frac{1}{2} \times 0.14 \times v^2$ or $2.38 = 0.07 \times v^2$
$2.38 \div 0.07 = v^2$ so $v^2 = 34$

Step 4) Square root: $v = \sqrt{34} = \underline{5.83 \text{ m/s}}$

Easy peasy? Not really, no, but if you practise using the four steps you'll find it's not too bad.

Most Energy Transfers Involve Some Losses, Often as Heat

1) Every time energy is <u>transferred</u> from one form to another, some of the energy is <u>lost</u> to the surroundings — often as <u>heat</u>, and sometimes as <u>sound</u>. For example, in a car you want all the <u>chemical energy</u> of the fuel to be transferred into <u>kinetic energy</u>, but the car <u>warms up</u> and makes a <u>load of noise</u>, so some energy is lost as heat and sound.

2) Heat energy is <u>transferred</u> to <u>cooler</u> surroundings, which then become <u>warmer</u>. As the heat is <u>transferred</u> to cooler surroundings, the <u>energy</u> becomes <u>less concentrated</u> — it dissipates.

3) According to the <u>Principle of Conservation of Energy</u>, the <u>total</u> amount of <u>energy</u> stays the <u>same</u>. So the energy is still there, but it <u>can't be easily used</u> or <u>collected back in</u> again.

Conserve your energy — you'll need it for the next page...

<u>Rollercoasters</u> are a good example of the conversion of <u>gravitational potential energy</u> into <u>kinetic energy</u> — and one that pops up in exams time and time again. Just remember that some of the energy will be <u>wasted as heat</u>.

Radioactivity

Not every atom of an element is stable — and unstable atoms give out radiation. But we'll get onto that towards the end of the page. First up, a nifty way to write the number of protons and neutrons in an atom...

Elements can be Described Using Atomic and Mass Numbers

We can describe how many protons and neutrons there are in the nucleus of an atom of a particular element using this handy form...

EXAMPLE: OXYGEN

THE MASS (NUCLEON) NUMBER ———— 16
— total of protons and neutrons

THE ATOMIC (PROTON) NUMBER ———— 8
— number of protons

O

O is the chemical symbol for oxygen.

Isotopes are Different Forms of the Same Element

1) Isotopes are atoms with the same number of protons in their nucleus, but a different number of neutrons.

2) Hence they have the same atomic number, but different mass numbers.

3) Carbon-12 and carbon-14 are good examples:

4) Most elements have different isotopes, but there's usually only one or two stable ones (like carbon-12).

5) The other isotopes tend to be radioactive (like carbon-14) which means they decay into other elements and give out radiation. This is where all radioactivity comes from — unstable radioactive isotopes undergoing nuclear decay and spitting out high-energy particles or waves.

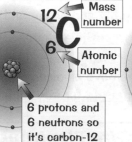

$^{12}_{6}C$ Mass number / Atomic number — 6 protons and 6 neutrons so it's carbon-12

$^{14}_{6}C$ — 6 protons and 8 neutrons so it's carbon-14

Radioactivity is a Totally Random Process

1) Unstable nuclei will decay and in the process give out ionising radiation (see below).

2) This process is entirely random. This means that if you have 1000 unstable nuclei, you can't say when any one of them is going to decay, nor can you do anything at all to make a decay happen.

3) When the nucleus does decay it will spit out one or more of three types of radiation — alpha, beta or gamma (see next page). In the process, the nucleus will often change into a new element.

Alpha, Beta and Gamma Radiation can Cause Ionisation

1) Atoms can gain or lose electrons. When an atom (with no overall charge) loses or gains an electron it is turned into an ion (which is charged). This is known as ionisation.

2) Alpha, beta and gamma are all types of ionising radiation — they can cause ionisation of atoms.

3) Alpha particles have a large positive charge. When an alpha particle passes close to an atom, it can pull a negatively-charged electron out of orbit.

4) Beta particles (which are negatively charged) cause ionisation in a similar way to alpha particles. But instead of pulling an electron out of orbit, they push it out (as like charges repel each other, see p.44).

5) Gamma rays can interact with the electrons orbiting an atom and transfer energy to them. If the electron gets enough energy, it can break free from the atom.

 I'm free!

See the next page for info on how well alpha, beta and gamma ionise.

Completely random — just like your revision shouldn't be...

It's the number of protons which decides what element something is, then the number of neutrons decides what isotope of that element it is. And it's unstable isotopes which undergo radioactive decay and give out radiation — alpha, beta or gamma. There's lots more to know about those three — the next page is packed full of fun facts.

Radioactivity

What's that? You'd love to hear more about the <u>properties</u> of <u>alpha</u>, <u>beta</u> and <u>gamma radiation</u>?
Well, since you asked so nicely...

Alpha, Beta and Gamma Radiation Have Different Properties

You need to remember <u>three things</u> about <u>each type of radiation</u>:

1) What it <u>actually is</u>.

2) How strongly it <u>ionises</u> a material (i.e. removes electrons from atoms — see page 63).

3) How well it <u>penetrates</u> materials.

There's a pattern: the <u>more ionising</u> the radiation is, the <u>less penetrating</u> it is. Strongly ionising radiation
<u>gives up its energy quickly</u> as it creates <u>ions</u> — so they <u>don't penetrate far</u> into materials.

Alpha Particles are Helium Nuclei

$^{4}_{2}\text{He}$

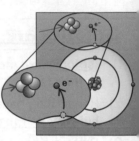

Their slow speed means they take longer to pass by an atom, which increases the chance of ionisation.

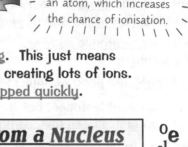

1) They're made up of <u>two protons</u> and <u>two neutrons</u>.

2) They are relatively <u>big</u> and <u>heavy</u> and <u>slow-moving</u>.

3) They have a <u>strong positive charge</u>.

4) Their big mass and charge make them <u>strongly ionising</u>. This just means
they are able to remove electrons from lots of atoms, creating lots of ions.
So they <u>don't penetrate</u> far into materials, but are <u>stopped quickly</u>.

Beta Particles are Electrons Emitted from a Nucleus

$^{0}_{-1}\text{e}$

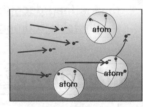

1) These are <u>in between alpha and gamma</u> in terms of their <u>properties</u>.

2) They move <u>quite fast</u> and they are <u>quite small</u> (they're electrons).

3) They have a <u>negative charge</u>.

4) They are <u>moderately ionising</u> and <u>penetrate moderately</u> far into
materials (further than alpha particles) before being <u>stopped</u>.

5) For every <u>beta-particle</u> emitted, a <u>neutron</u> turns to a <u>proton</u> in the nucleus.

Gamma Rays are a Type of Electromagnetic Radiation

1) They are the <u>opposite of alpha particles</u> in a way.

2) They are <u>weakly ionising</u> and can <u>penetrate a long way</u> into
materials before <u>eventually</u> interacting with an atom.

Remember What Blocks the Three Types of Radiation...

<u>Alpha particles</u> are blocked by <u>paper</u> and <u>cardboard</u>.
<u>Beta particles</u> are blocked by thin <u>aluminium</u>.
<u>Gamma rays</u> are blocked by <u>thick lead</u>.

Of course anything <u>equivalent</u> will also block them,
e.g. <u>skin</u> will stop <u>alpha</u>, but <u>not</u> the others; a thin sheet
of <u>any metal</u> will stop <u>beta</u>; and <u>very thick concrete</u> will
stop <u>gamma</u> just like lead does.

Paper or cardboard stops ALPHA

Thin aluminium stops BETA

Thick lead stops GAMMA

Don't let alpha particles upset you — be a bit more thick-skinned...

So, three things to learn about each type of ionising radiation — what it is, how ionising it is and how well it
penetrates materials. Nothing too taxing on the brain, I reckon. It's the different <u>properties</u> of these types of
radiation that make them suitable for <u>different purposes</u> — but you'll find out more about that later on...

Nuclear Fission

It's amazing how much <u>energy</u> there is <u>trapped</u> in a little atom. This energy is released by <u>nuclear fission</u>.

Nuclear Fission — The Splitting Up of Uranium Atoms

<u>Nuclear fission</u> is a type of <u>nuclear reaction</u> that is used to <u>release energy</u> from uranium (or plutonium) atoms, e.g. in a nuclear reactor. <u>Huge amounts</u> of energy can be released this way by using a <u>chain reaction</u>...

The Chain Reaction:

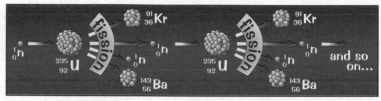

1) A <u>slow-moving neutron</u> is fired at an isotope of uranium — uranium-235. The neutron is <u>absorbed</u> by the nucleus — this makes the atom unstable and causes it to split.

2) When the U-235 atom splits it forms <u>two new lighter</u> elements ('<u>daughter nuclei</u>') and <u>thermal</u> (heat) <u>energy</u> is released.

A neutron is <u>absorbed</u> by the nucleus because it has <u>no charge</u> — i.e. it's not <u>repelled</u> by the positive charge of the nucleus.

3) There are lots of different pairs of atoms that uranium can split into, e.g. krypton-91 and barium-143, but all these new nuclei are <u>radioactive</u> because they have the '<u>wrong</u>' number of neutrons in them (see p.90).

4) Each time a <u>uranium</u> atom <u>splits up</u>, it also spits out <u>two or three neutrons</u>, which can hit <u>other</u> uranium nuclei, causing them to <u>split</u> also, and so on and so on. This is a <u>chain reaction</u>.

Nuclear Power Stations are Really Glorified Steam Engines

Nuclear power stations are powered by <u>nuclear reactors</u>. In a nuclear reactor, a <u>controlled chain reaction</u> takes place in which uranium atoms <u>split up</u>. The <u>heat energy</u> released by nuclear fission is used to <u>boil water</u> to drive a <u>steam turbine</u>, which turns a <u>generator</u> to generate <u>electrical energy</u>.

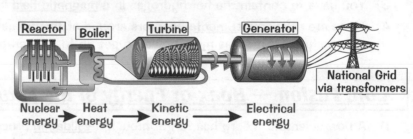

Chain Reactions in Reactors Must be Carefully Controlled

1) The <u>neutrons</u> released by fission reactions in a nuclear reactor have <u>a lot</u> of energy. These neutrons will only cause <u>other</u> nuclear fissions (and cause a chain reaction) if they are <u>moving slow</u> enough to be <u>captured</u> by the uranium nuclei in the fuel rods.

2) To do this, the uranium <u>fuel rods</u> are placed in a <u>moderator</u> (for example, water) to <u>slow down</u> the fast moving neutrons.

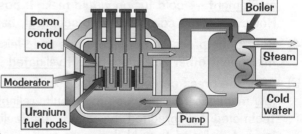

3) This creates a <u>steady rate</u> of nuclear fission, where <u>one new neutron</u> produces another fission.

4) <u>Control rods</u>, often made of <u>boron</u>, limit the rate of fission by <u>absorbing</u> excess neutrons. They are placed <u>in between</u> the fuel rods and are <u>raised</u> and <u>lowered</u> into the reactor to <u>control</u> the chain reaction.

5) If the chain reaction in a nuclear reactor is <u>left to continue unchecked</u>, large amounts of <u>energy</u> are <u>released</u> in a very <u>short time</u>. <u>Many new fissions</u> will follow each fission, causing a <u>runaway reaction</u> which could lead to an <u>explosion</u>.

Revise nuclear power — full steam ahead...

When nuclear fission is used to produce energy in power stations, the chain reaction has to be <u>controlled</u> so that <u>safe</u> amounts of energy are released. More of a problem are the <u>radioactive products</u> (see page 71).

Nuclear Fusion

Loads of energy's released either when you break apart <u>really big nuclei</u> or join together <u>really small nuclei</u>. You can't do much with the ones in the middle, I'm afraid. (Don't ask, you don't want to know.)

Nuclear Fusion — The Joining of Small Atomic Nuclei

1) <u>Nuclear fusion</u> is the opposite of nuclear fission.

2) In nuclear fusion, two <u>light nuclei collide</u> at high speed and <u>join</u> (fuse) to create a <u>larger</u> nucleus. For example, <u>hydrogen</u> nuclei can fuse to produce <u>helium nuclei</u>.

3) Fusion releases <u>a lot</u> of <u>energy</u> (<u>more</u> than fission for a given mass) — all the energy released in <u>stars</u> comes from fusion. So people are trying to develop <u>fusion reactors</u> to make <u>electricity</u>.

4) Fusion <u>doesn't</u> leave behind a lot of radioactive <u>waste</u> (see p.71) and there's <u>plenty</u> of hydrogen knocking about to use as <u>fuel</u>.

Fusion Only Happens at High Temperatures and Pressure

1) The <u>big problem</u> is that fusion only happens at <u>really high pressures and temperatures</u> (about <u>10 000 000 °C</u>). It doesn't happen at <u>low temperatures</u> and <u>pressures</u> due to the <u>electrostatic repulsion</u> of <u>protons</u> (like charges repel each other, see p.44).

2) It's <u>really hard</u> to create the <u>right conditions</u> for fusion. <u>No material</u> can withstand that kind of temperature — it would just be <u>vaporised</u>. So fusion reactors are <u>really hard</u> and <u>expensive</u> to try to build.

3) You have to contain the hot hydrogen in a <u>magnetic field</u> instead of a physical container.

4) There are a few <u>experimental</u> reactors around at the moment, but none of them are generating electricity yet. It takes <u>more</u> power to get up to temperature than the reactor can produce.

BEWARE: the filling of this fruit pie is hotter than the conditions needed for fusion

Cold Fusion — Hoax or Energy of the Future?

1) A new scientific theory has to go through a <u>validation</u> process before it's accepted. This means making the <u>research results public</u> — usually in a <u>journal</u> such as <u>Nature</u>, so that other scientists can <u>repeat</u> the experiments. If lots of scientists get the <u>same results</u>, the theory is likely to be <u>accepted</u>.

2) An example of a theory which <u>hasn't</u> been accepted yet is '<u>cold fusion</u>'. Cold fusion is <u>nuclear fusion</u> which occurs at around <u>room temperature</u>, rather than at millions of degrees Celsius.

3) In 1989 two scientists, <u>Stanley Pons</u> and <u>Martin Fleischmann</u>, reported to a press conference that they had succeeded in releasing energy from cold fusion, using a simple experiment. This caused a lot of <u>excitement</u> — cold fusion would make it possible to generate lots of electricity, easily and cheaply. However, many scientists were <u>sceptical</u>, believing that fusion is only possible at very high temperatures.

4) Before the press conference, Pons and Fleischmann's work hadn't been <u>peer reviewed</u> — this meant other scientists hadn't <u>validated</u> their work before they went public.

5) After the press conference, other scientists tried to <u>repeat</u> Pons and Fleichmann's work. But <u>few</u> managed to reproduce the results <u>reliably</u>. When a group at <u>MIT</u> (Massachusetts Institute of Technology) <u>discredited</u> the theory, the feeling against cold fusion was so strong that some scientific journals <u>refused to publish</u> papers on it.

6) Despite all the setbacks, there is still <u>funding</u> available for cold fusion research, and Pons and Fleischmann's results have actually been <u>repeated</u> many times now — although <u>not reliably enough</u> for the theory to be accepted by the scientific community.

Pity they can't release energy by confusion...*

At about the same time as research started on fusion reactors, physicists were working on a <u>fusion bomb</u>. These "hydrogen bombs" are incredibly powerful — they can release a few thousand times more energy than the nuclear fission bombs that destroyed Hiroshima and Nagasaki at the end of World War II.

Background Radiation and Half-life

We're constantly exposed to <u>very low levels</u> of radiation — and all without us noticing. Sneaky.

Background Radiation Comes from Many Sources

<u>Background radiation</u> is the <u>low-level</u> radiation that's around us <u>all the time</u>. Background radiation comes from:

1) Radioactivity of naturally occurring <u>unstable isotopes</u> which are <u>all around us</u> — in the <u>air</u>, in <u>food</u>, in <u>building materials</u> and in the <u>rocks</u> under our feet.

2) Radiation from <u>space</u>, which is known as <u>cosmic rays</u>. These come mostly from the <u>Sun</u>. Luckily, the Earth's <u>atmosphere protects</u> us from much of this radiation, and its <u>magnetic field</u> deflects cosmic rays away from us.

3) Radiation due to <u>human activity</u>, e.g. <u>fallout</u> from <u>nuclear explosions</u> or <u>dumped nuclear waste</u> (see p.71). But this represents a <u>tiny</u> proportion of the total background radiation.

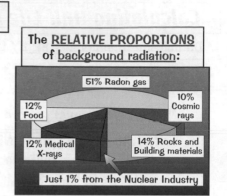

The <u>RELATIVE PROPORTIONS</u> of <u>background radiation</u>:

51% Radon gas
10% Cosmic rays
12% Food
12% Medical X-rays
14% Rocks and Building materials
Just 1% from the Nuclear Industry

The Level of Background Radiation Changes Depending on Where You Are

1) Certain <u>underground rocks</u> (e.g. granite) can cause higher levels of background radiation at the <u>surface</u>, especially if they release <u>radioactive radon gas</u>, which tends to get <u>trapped inside people's houses</u>.

2) The <u>radon concentration</u> in people's houses <u>varies widely</u> across the UK, depending on the type of <u>rock</u> the house is built on.

3) So, the amount of <u>radon gas</u> that people are exposed to also depends on the <u>region</u> of the country they're living in.

Millom

Coloured bits indicate more radiation from rocks

The Radioactivity of a Source Always Decreases Over Time

The <u>activity</u> of a radioactive source <u>decreases</u> over time, <u>regardless</u> of what the source is.

1) Each time a radioactive nucleus <u>decays</u> (see page 63), and radiation is emitted, one more <u>radioactive nucleus disappears</u>.

2) As the <u>unstable nuclei</u> all steadily disappear, the <u>activity as a whole</u> will <u>decrease</u>. So the <u>older</u> a source becomes, the <u>less radiation</u> it will emit.

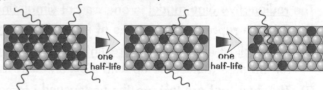

one half-life   one half-life

3) For <u>some</u> isotopes it takes <u>just a few hours</u> before nearly all the unstable nuclei have <u>decayed</u>, whilst others last for <u>millions of years</u>.

4) The problem with trying to <u>measure</u> this is that <u>the activity never reaches zero</u>, which is why we have to use the idea of <u>half-life</u> to measure how quickly the activity <u>drops off</u>.

> The <u>HALF-LIFE</u> of a radioactive isotope is the <u>TIME TAKEN</u> for <u>HALF</u> of the <u>undecayed nuclei</u> to <u>DECAY</u>.

5) A <u>short half-life</u> means the <u>activity falls quickly</u>, because <u>lots</u> of the nuclei decay <u>quickly</u>.

6) A <u>long half-life</u> means the activity <u>falls more slowly</u> because <u>most</u> of the nuclei don't decay <u>for a long time</u> — they just sit there, <u>basically unstable</u>, but kind of <u>biding their time</u>.

7) The <u>activity</u> of a radioactive isotope is measured in <u>becquerels</u> (Bq). <u>1 Bq</u> is <u>1 decay per second</u>. This can be measured with a <u>Geiger-Muller</u> (G-M) tube.

Background radiation — the ugly wallpaper of the Universe...

Background radiation was discovered <u>accidentally</u>. Scientists were measuring radioactivity of materials, but they detected radioactivity when there was <u>no material</u> being tested. They realised it must be natural background radiation.

Calculating Half-life

Half-life is a tricky concept, but it can be calculated quite simply by looking at the activity of a sample over time.

Calculating Half-Life is Best Done Step by Step

Do half-life questions **STEP BY STEP**. Like this one:

A VERY SIMPLE EXAMPLE: The activity of a radioisotope is 640 Bq.
Two hours later it has fallen to 40 Bq. Find the half-life of the sample.

ANSWER: You must go through it in short simple steps like this:

INITIAL count:	after ONE half-life:	after TWO half-lives:	after THREE half-lives:	after FOUR half-lives:
640 (÷2) →	320 (÷2) →	160 (÷2) →	80 (÷2) →	40

Notice the careful step-by-step method, which tells us it takes four half-lives for the activity to fall from 640 to 40. Hence two hours represents four half-lives, so the half-life is 30 minutes.

Measuring the Half-Life of a Source Using a Graph

1) This can only be done by taking several readings of the source's activity, usually using a G-M tube and counter (p.67).

2) The results can then be plotted as a graph, which will always be shaped like the one to the right.

3) The half-life is found from the graph, by finding the time interval on the bottom axis corresponding to a halving of the activity on the vertical axis. Easy peasy really.

4) One trick you need to know is about the background radiation (p.67), which also enters the G-M tube and gives false readings. Measure the background count first and then subtract it from every reading you get, before plotting the results on the graph.

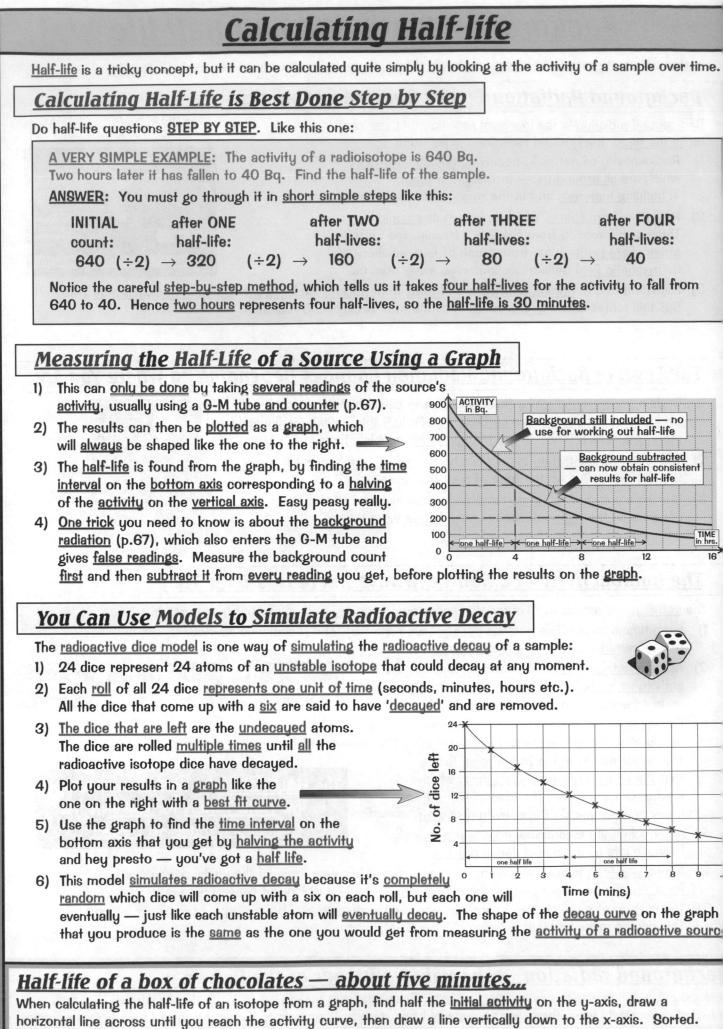

You Can Use Models to Simulate Radioactive Decay

The radioactive dice model is one way of simulating the radioactive decay of a sample:

1) 24 dice represent 24 atoms of an unstable isotope that could decay at any moment.

2) Each roll of all 24 dice represents one unit of time (seconds, minutes, hours etc.). All the dice that come up with a six are said to have 'decayed' and are removed.

3) The dice that are left are the undecayed atoms. The dice are rolled multiple times until all the radioactive isotope dice have decayed.

4) Plot your results in a graph like the one on the right with a best fit curve.

5) Use the graph to find the time interval on the bottom axis that you get by halving the activity and hey presto — you've got a half life.

6) This model simulates radioactive decay because it's completely random which dice will come up with a six on each roll, but each one will eventually — just like each unstable atom will eventually decay. The shape of the decay curve on the graph that you produce is the same as the one you would get from measuring the activity of a radioactive source.

Half-life of a box of chocolates — about five minutes...

When calculating the half-life of an isotope from a graph, find half the initial activity on the y-axis, draw a horizontal line across until you reach the activity curve, then draw a line vertically down to the x-axis. Sorted.

Uses of Radioactivity

With radioactive sources belting out all those emissions, some clever scientists thought up some uses for it all.

Household Fire Alarms — Use Alpha Radiation

1) A <u>weak</u> source of alpha radiation (p.64) is placed in a smoke detector, close to <u>two electrodes</u>.
2) The source causes <u>ionisation</u>, and a <u>current</u> flows.
3) If there is a fire then smoke will <u>absorb</u> the radiation
   — the current stops and the <u>alarm sounds</u>.

Sterilisation of Food and Equipment Using Gamma Rays

1) <u>Food</u> can be <u>irradiated with</u> (exposed to) a <u>high dose</u> of <u>gamma rays</u> which will <u>kill</u> all <u>microbes</u>. This means that the food doesn't go bad as quickly as it would do otherwise.
2) Similarly, <u>medical equipment</u> can be <u>sterilised</u> using gamma rays instead of being <u>boiled</u>.

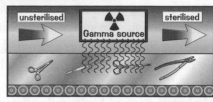

3) <u>Irradiation</u> is a particularly good method of sterilisation because, unlike boiling, it doesn't involve <u>high temperatures</u>, so <u>fresh fruit</u> or <u>plastic instruments</u> can be totally <u>sterilised</u> without being <u>damaged</u>.
4) The radioactive source used for this needs to be a <u>very strong</u> emitter of <u>gamma rays</u> with a <u>reasonably long half-life</u> (at least several months) so that it doesn't need <u>replacing</u> too often.

Radiation is Used in Tracers and Thickness Gauges

1) Certain radioactive isotopes can be used as <u>tracers</u>. A <u>medical</u> tracer is <u>injected</u> into a patient (or <u>swallowed</u>) and its progress around the body is followed using an <u>external detector</u>. A <u>computer</u> uses the reading from the detector to produce an <u>image</u> to follow the flow of the injected isotope. This method can be used to <u>detect</u> and <u>diagnose medical conditions</u> (e.g. cancer).
2) <u>All isotopes</u> which are taken <u>into the body</u> must be <u>BETA or GAMMA</u> emitters (never alpha), so that the radiation <u>passes out of the body</u> — and they should only last <u>a few hours</u>, so that the radioactivity inside the patient <u>quickly disappears</u> (i.e. they should have a <u>short half-life</u>).
3) <u>Gamma emitting tracers</u> are also used in <u>industry</u> to detect <u>leaks</u> in <u>underground pipes</u>.
4) <u>Beta radiation</u> is used in <u>thickness control</u>. You direct radiation through the stuff being made (e.g. paper), and put a detector on the other side, connected to a control unit. When the amount of <u>detected</u> radiation changes, it means the paper is coming out too thick or too thin, so the control unit adjusts the rollers to give the correct thickness.

5) The radioactive source used needs to have a fairly long half-life so it doesn't decay away <u>too quickly</u>.
6) It also needs to be a <u>beta</u> source, because then the paper will <u>partly block</u> the radiation (see p.64). If it <u>all</u> goes through (or <u>none</u> of it does), then the reading <u>won't change</u> at all as the thickness changes.

Gamma Rays Can Be Used to Treat Cancer

1) High doses of gamma rays will <u>kill all living cells</u>. For this reason, they can be used to <u>treat cancers</u>.
2) <u>Radiotherapists</u> have to be very careful when treating a patient to <u>direct</u> the gamma rays right at the <u>cancerous</u> cells, so they can <u>minimise</u> the damage done to <u>healthy</u> cells.

Ionising radiation — just what the doctor ordered...

Radiation has many important uses — especially in <u>medicine</u>. Make sure you know which type of radiation is used in each application and why. Examiners just love to ask you questions on this stuff.

Dangers of Radioactivity

Attitudes towards the dangers of radioactivity changed a lot over the last century.

1) When Marie Curie discovered the radioactive properties of radium in 1898, nobody knew anything about its dangers. People were fascinated by radium — it was used in medicines and to make luminous paint. You could buy everyday products made using this paint, e.g. glow-in-the-dark watches.

2) However, by the 1930s people were starting to link health problems to radiation — many watch dial painters developed cancer as a result of exposure to radium. More recently, we've learnt a lot about the dangers of radiation from the long-term effects of terrible events like the nuclear attacks on Japan in 1945 and the Chernobyl disaster in 1986.

Ionising Radiation Can Cause Tissue Damage and Cell Mutation

Alpha, beta and gamma radiation will cheerfully enter living cells and collide with molecules of genetic material. These collisions cause ionisation, which leads to tissue damage.

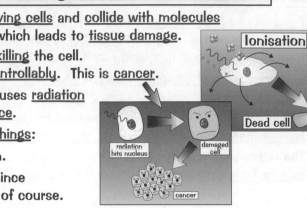

1) Lower doses tend to cause minor damage without killing the cell. This can give rise to mutant cells which divide uncontrollably. This is cancer.

2) Higher doses tend to kill cells completely, which causes radiation sickness if a lot of body cells all get battered at once.

3) The extent of the harmful effects depends on two things:

   a) How much exposure you have to the radiation.

   b) The energy and penetration of the radiation, since some types are more hazardous than others, of course.

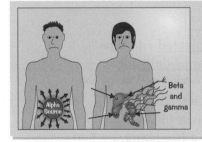

Outside the body, beta and gamma sources are the most dangerous. This is because beta and gamma can get inside to the delicate organs, whereas alpha is much less dangerous because it can't penetrate the skin. Inside the body, an alpha source is the most dangerous. Alpha sources do all their damage in a very localised area. Beta and gamma sources on the other hand are less dangerous inside the body because they mostly pass straight out without doing much damage.

You Should Protect Yourself in the Laboratory...

You should always act to minimise your exposure to radioactive sources.

1) Never allow skin contact with a source. Always handle sources with tongs.

2) Keep the source at arm's length to keep it as far from the body as possible.

3) Keep the source pointing away from the body and avoid looking directly at it.

4) Always put the source back in a labelled lead box, as soon as the experiment is over, to keep your exposure time short.

...and If You Work with Nuclear Radiation

1) Industrial nuclear workers wear full protective suits to prevent tiny radioactive particles being inhaled or lodging on the skin or under fingernails etc.

2) Lead-lined suits, lead/concrete barriers and thick lead screens are used to prevent exposure to gamma rays from highly contaminated areas (alpha and beta radiation are stopped much more easily — see p.64).

3) Workers use remote-controlled robot arms to carry out tasks in highly radioactive areas.

Revision sickness — never mind, it'll wear off...

It's quite difficult to do research on how radiation affects humans. This is partly because it would be very unethical to do controlled experiments, exposing people to huge doses of radiation just to see what happens. We rely mostly on studies of populations affected by nuclear accidents or nuclear bombs.

Nuclear Power

Nuclear power may be the best solution to future electricity supply problems, but it is a very <u>controversial</u> area for science. Intrigued? I bet you are. Get reading to find out more...

Nuclear Waste is a Big Problem for the Nuclear Industry

1) <u>Nuclear fission</u> releases a lot of energy that can be used to generate electricity (see page 65), but it also creates <u>radioactive waste products</u> that can't just be <u>thrown away</u>.

2) The waste products from nuclear fission <u>can't</u> usually be recycled to create more electricity. They also have <u>very long half-lives</u>, meaning they will be <u>radioactive</u> for <u>hundreds</u> or even <u>thousands</u> (or millions) of <u>years</u>.

3) This radioactive waste can be <u>really dangerous</u> (see previous page) so it needs to be put somewhere <u>far away</u> from <u>people</u> to stop it causing any <u>harm</u>.

4) At the moment, nuclear power stations usually deal with the most dangerous nuclear waste by <u>vitrification</u> — this means they melt the waste with other materials to form a type of <u>glass</u>. The liquid glass is sealed inside <u>steel canisters</u> and buried deep <u>underground</u>.

5) Another way to deal with nuclear waste is to pack it into <u>thick metal containers</u> and/or bury the waste in a deep hole and then fill the hole with <u>tons of concrete</u>.

6) Generally, the important thing when you're <u>storing</u> nuclear waste is to make sure there are plenty of materials to <u>absorb the radiation</u> long before it can reach the surface of the Earth.

Using Nuclear Power Has Its Pros and Cons

Nuclear power has a lot going for it, but some people are completely against it being used.

1) <u>Public perception</u> of nuclear power can be <u>very negative</u> — it's often seen by many to be <u>very dangerous</u>.

2) Some people worry that nuclear waste can <u>never be disposed of safely</u>. There is always a danger that the nuclear waste could <u>leak out</u> and <u>pollute</u> land, rivers and oceans. In the past there have been <u>serious accidents</u> that have <u>contaminated huge areas</u> with radioactivity. Some people say that the energy generated by nuclear power is <u>not worth the risk</u> of nuclear waste accidents.

3) <u>Nuclear power</u> also carries the risk of <u>leaks</u> from the power station or a <u>major catastrophe</u> like <u>Chernobyl</u>.

4) However, nuclear power is generally a <u>pretty safe</u> way of generating electricity — it's not as <u>risky</u> as <u>some people may think</u> it is.

5) And it's not all doom and gloom. Nuclear power is a <u>very reliable</u> energy resource and reduces the need for fossil fuels (which are already running out — see p.34).

6) <u>Fossil fuels</u> (coal, oil and gas) all release carbon dioxide (CO_2) when they're burnt. This adds to the <u>greenhouse effect</u> and <u>global warming</u>. Burning coal and oil also releases <u>sulphur dioxide</u> that can cause <u>acid rain</u>. Nuclear power <u>doesn't</u> release these gases, so in this way it is a very <u>clean</u> source of energy.

7) <u>Huge</u> amounts of energy can be generated from a relatively <u>small</u> amount of <u>nuclear material</u>. Nuclear <u>fuel</u> (i.e. the uranium) is <u>cheap</u> and <u>readily available</u>.

8) However, the <u>overall cost</u> of nuclear power is <u>high</u> due to the initial cost of the <u>power plant</u> and final <u>decommissioning</u> — dismantling a nuclear plant safely takes <u>decades</u>.

Eating radioactive sheep? That's probably bad for ewe...

In 1986 the <u>Chernobyl</u> nuclear power plant in Ukraine overheated when too many of the <u>control rods</u> were removed in a system test. The resulting explosions released <u>100 times</u> the radiation of the bombs that were dropped on Japan, and nearby cities had to be totally evacuated. Today, the areas around Chernobyl <u>remain deserted</u>.

Revision Summary for P2b Topics 4, 5 & 6

Right, you've conquered three revision topics — time to see if any of it has stuck. Good luck chaps.

1)   What are the two different parts of the overall stopping distance of a car?

2)   List two factors which affect each of the two parts of the stopping distance.

3)* Write down the formula for momentum. Find the momentum of a 78 kg sheep falling at 15 m/s.

4)* A gymnast (mass 50 kg) jumps off a beam and hits the floor at a speed of 7 m/s.
     She bends her knees and stops moving in 0.5 s. What is the average force acting on her?

5)   Explain how seat belts, crumple zones and airbags are useful in a crash.

6)   What's the connection between 'work done' and 'energy transferred'?

7)* Write down the formula for work done. A crazy dog drags a big branch 12 m over the next-door
     neighbour's front lawn, pulling with a force of 535 N. How much energy is transferred?

8)   What's the formula for power? What are the units of power?

9)* An electric motor transfers 540 kJ of electrical energy in 4½ minutes. What is its power output?

10)* What's the formula for kinetic energy? Find the kinetic energy of a 78 kg sheep moving at 23 m/s.

11)* Write down the formula for gravitational potential energy. Calculate the increase in gravitational potential
     energy when a box of mass 12 kg is raised through 4.5 m. (Assume g = 10 N/kg.)

12)* A roller coaster train of mass 15 000 kg starts from the top of a hill. As it travels down the hill it drops a
     vertical distance of 50 m. How much gravitational potential energy does it lose in this time?

13) Write down the principle of the conservation of energy.

14)* Assuming no air resistance, calculate the kinetic energy of a 78 kg sheep just as it hits the floor after
     falling from a height of 20 m. How fast is the sheep travelling as it hits the floor?

15) Explain what the mass number and atomic number of an atom represent.

16) Write down the number of protons and neutrons in an atom of $^{230}_{90}$Th.

17) Explain what isotopes are. Give an example. Do stable or unstable isotopes undergo nuclear decay?

18) Describe in detail the nature and properties of the three types of ionising radiation:
     a) alpha,   b) beta,   c) gamma.

19) Name a substance that will block each of the three types of nuclear radiation.

20) What type of particle is U-235 bombarded with to make it split?

21) Draw a diagram to illustrate the fission of uranium-235 and explain how the chain reaction works.

22) Explain in terms of energy transfers how electricity is produced in a nuclear power station.

23) What is nuclear fusion? Why is it difficult to construct a working fusion reactor?

24) What is 'cold fusion'? Why are many scientists still sceptical about cold fusion as a
     way of releasing energy?

25) Describe the process that new scientific theories have to go through before they are accepted.

26) Give three sources of background radiation.

27) Give a proper definition of half-life.

28) Sketch a typical graph of activity against time for a radioactive source.
     Show how you can find the half-life from your graph.

29)* The activity of a radioisotope sample is 840 Bq. Four hours later it has fallen to 105 Bq.
     Find the half-life of the sample.

30) Describe in detail how radioactive sources are used in each of the following:
     a) smoke detectors,   b) sterilisation of food,   c) tracers in medicine,   d) treating cancer.

31) Explain what kind of damage ionising radiation causes to body cells. What are the effects of high doses?
     What damage can lower doses do?

32) Which kinds of radioactive source are most dangerous: a) inside the body, b) outside the body?

33) List four safety precautions that should be taken when handling radioactive materials in the school lab.

34) Give one reason for using nuclear power rather than fossil fuels.

35) What is the main environmental problem associated with nuclear power?

Medical Physics and Ultrasound

Medical physicists develop new ways of using physics in medicine to help doctors solve medical problems. Physics is used in medical imaging to diagnose problems, and in treatments such as radiotherapy.

Ionising and Non-ionising Radiation are Both Used in Medicine

You remember ionising radiation — those high energy particles or waves that rush into things, knocking electrons hither and thither... No? Well head back to page 20 for a quick refresher.

Both ionising and non-ionising radiation are used by doctors and medical physicists. Their use in medicine isn't always straightforward — compromises have to be made. For example, sometimes ionising radiation can give you a fantastically clear image of inside the body, but it does risk damage to the patient's cells (see p. 70).

X-rays are used for Medical Imaging

X-rays are high energy EM waves that get absorbed by dense materials like bone and metal. Radiographers use their properties to take X-ray photographs that can be used to diagnose things like bone fractures. X-rays are one type of ionising radiation (see p.84) which means there's a health risk to people who are exposed to them.

CAT Scans use X-rays

Computerised axial tomography (CAT) scans use X-rays to produce an image of a two-dimensional slice through the body (p.85). CAT scans use intense beams of X-rays that are strongly ionising. Unlike standard X-ray photographs, they can be used to image soft tissue as well as bones.

Image of a "slice" through patient's head

Endoscopes Use Optical Fibres to See Inside the Body

Visible light is one type of non-ionising radiation used in modern medicine Endoscopes reflect light along optical fibres (see p.82) and can be used to see inside the patient to investigate problems without the need for invasive surgery. They can even be used for keyhole surgery.

Ultrasound is Sound with a Higher Frequency Than We Can Hear

Sound waves with frequencies above 20 kHz (beyond the range of human hearing) are called ultrasound (see p.28). Ultrasound is a non-ionising method of medical imaging, which means it's a lot safer for the patient than imaging using ionising radiation. Ultrasound has loads of medical uses, here are just a few:

Breaking down Kidney Stones

Kidney stones are hard masses that can block the urinary tract and be extremely painful. An ultrasound beam concentrates high energy waves at the kidney stone and turns it into sand-like particles. These particles then pass out of the body in urine. It's a good method because the patient doesn't need surgery and it's relatively painless.

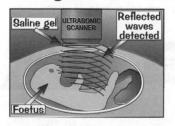

Saline gel | ULTRASONIC SCANNER | Reflected waves detected

Foetus

Pre-Natal Scanning of a Foetus

Ultrasound imaging can be used to diagnose soft tissue problems and to perform pre-natal scans of a foetus in the womb. The ultrasound waves are reflected off the different tissue boundaries, and the times and distributions of the echoes are processed by a computer to form an image on a screen.

Measuring the Speed of Blood Flow

Because ultrasound works in real time it can show things changing and moving. This makes it useful for investigating problems with blood flow — particularly in the heart and liver. Special ultrasound machines can measure the speed of blood flow and identify any blockages in the veins and arteries.

What did the X-ray say to the muscle? Just passing through...

Crikey, there are lots of different uses of physics in medicine. Make sure you learn all the examples above. Good-o.

Intensity of Radiation

Aaargghhh... radiation — we're all gonna die... *ahem*. Yes, it's high time to get some facts straight on the matter, I reckon. What is radiation, and how do you calculate its <u>intensity</u> — answers comin' up...

Radiation is Energy Emitted from a Source

The word 'radiation' is fairly common in physics lessons and in everyday life.
It's often used to refer to <u>ionising nuclear radiation</u> (e.g. alpha, beta and gamma radiation, see p.20) — but 'radiation' actually covers a lot more than that.

Learn this <u>really incredibly simple definition:</u> ▶ Radiation is <u>energy</u> that originates from a <u>source</u>.

This definition covers <u>all types of radiation</u> in physics — e.g. <u>light</u> emitted from a star or <u>alpha radiation</u> spreading from a radioactive isotope. Radiation can be in the form of a <u>wave</u> (e.g. X-rays, visible light, infrared radiation) or a <u>particle</u> (e.g. alpha particles, positrons, neutrons).

Intensity of Radiation Depends on Distance from Source...

Think of a heater or flame emitting <u>infrared radiation</u>. The <u>intensity of radiation decreases</u> as the <u>distance</u> from the source <u>increases</u>. You can tell that yourself, because the <u>further away</u> you are from the heat source, the <u>less heat</u> energy you receive.

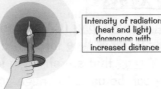

Intensity of radiation (heat and light) decreases with increased distance

...And on What it's Passing Through

1) The <u>intensity of radiation</u> also depends on the medium that it's <u>passing through</u>.
2) In practice, unless the radiation's passing through a <u>vacuum</u> (see p.15) <u>some of the radiation</u> will always be <u>absorbed</u> along the way by the <u>medium</u> it's passing through.
3) Generally, the more <u>dense</u> the medium, the more radiation will be <u>absorbed</u>, <u>decreasing</u> the intensity of the radiation.
4) Think about <u>sunglasses</u>. The dark glass <u>absorbs</u> some of the light, <u>reducing</u> its intensity.

Intensity = Power of Incident Radiation Per Unit Area

1) The <u>more intense</u> the radiation, the <u>more energy</u> it carries <u>per second</u>, or the higher the <u>power</u>. The higher the power, the <u>more energy</u> that gets <u>transferred</u> per second when it hits an object.
2) Obviously, the <u>surface area</u> of the object affects the <u>amount of radiation</u> that smacks into it. A big object is going to catch more radiation than a small one.
3) So, the intensity of radiation equals the <u>power of radiation</u> divided by the <u>area it falls on</u>: ▶ $\text{Intensity} = \dfrac{\text{Power}}{\text{Area}}$

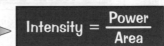

The units are W/m², unsurprisingly.

> **EXAMPLE:** The energy from a 100 W light bulb spreads over a surface of 4 m². Calculate the intensity of radiation.
> **ANSWER:** I = P/A = 100/4 = <u>25 W/m²</u>

What do you call X-ray emitting ketchup? A radiation sauce...

Man, this is intense. The fact is, there is radiation coming at you <u>all the time</u>, from the Sun, from your favourite fan heater — there's no escape... Most of the time there's no real need to worry though, radiation is just energy emitted from a source after all. And <u>only one formula</u> to memorise on this page — huzzah.

Lenses

I'm guessing you're pretty familiar with refraction by now — light waves bending blah blah blah... Anyways, things are about to get well interesting, 'cos we're gonna do refraction through lenses. Too jazzy by half.

Refraction is a Change in Direction Caused by a Change in Speed

Refraction is when radiation changes direction as it enters a different medium. This is caused by the change in density from one medium to the other — which changes the speed of the radiation.

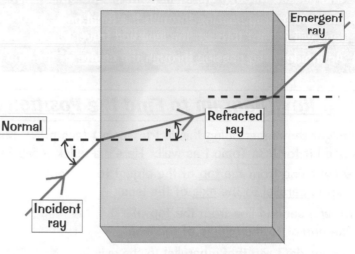

1) When waves of radiation slow down they bend towards the normal.

2) For example, when light enters glass or plastic it slows down — to about 2/3 of its speed in air.

3) If a wave hits a boundary at 90° (i.e. along the normal) it will not change direction — but it'll still slow down.

4) When a light hits a different medium (e.g. plastic or glass) some of the light will pass through the new medium but some will be reflected — it all depends on the angle of incidence (see p.12).

Different Lenses Produce Different Kinds of Image

There are two main types of lens — converging and diverging. They have different shapes and have opposite effects on light rays.

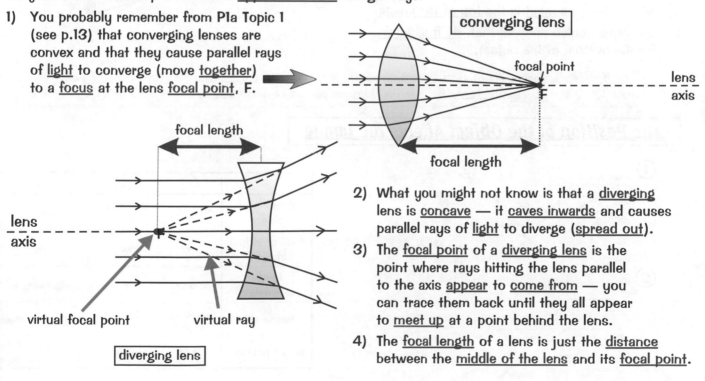

1) You probably remember from P1a Topic 1 (see p.13) that converging lenses are convex and that they cause parallel rays of light to converge (move together) to a focus at the lens focal point, F.

2) What you might not know is that a diverging lens is concave — it caves inwards and causes parallel rays of light to diverge (spread out).

3) The focal point of a diverging lens is the point where rays hitting the lens parallel to the axis appear to come from — you can trace them back until they all appear to meet up at a point behind the lens.

4) The focal length of a lens is just the distance between the middle of the lens and its focal point.

Warning — too much revision can cause attention to diverge...

OK, so refraction through lenses might not be the most thrilling part of physics, but the fact is it's well useful for optics... And also you have to learn it. The next few pages will show you just what some bent light rays can do.

Lenses

At some point in your life, you're going to need to be able to draw a ray diagram of refraction through a lens. When that day comes along, you'll be glad you followed these instructions <u>very carefully</u>...

There are Three Rules for Refraction in a Converging Lens

1) An incident ray <u>parallel to the axis</u> refracts through the lens and passes through the <u>focal point</u> on the other side.

2) An incident ray passing <u>through the focal point</u> before entering the lens will refract through the lens and travel <u>parallel to the axis</u>.

3) An incident ray passing through the <u>centre</u> of the lens carries on in the <u>same direction</u>.

Lenses have focal points on both sides.

Use a Ray Diagram to Find the Position and Size of an Image

You might remember doing this in P1a Topic 1 (see p.13), but what d'ya know, you need it for P3a Topic 1 as well. Here's a quick recap for your <u>revision pleasure</u>.

1) Draw a line from the <u>top</u> of the object to the lens that is <u>parallel</u> to the <u>axis</u> of the lens.

2) Draw a second line from the <u>top</u> of the object to the <u>middle</u> of the lens.

3) The incident ray that's <u>parallel</u> to the axis is <u>refracted</u> through the <u>focal point</u>. Draw a line representing the <u>refracted ray</u> passing through the <u>focal point</u> of the lens.

4) The ray passing through the <u>middle</u> of the lens doesn't bend, so continue the line <u>through the lens</u> and <u>out the other side</u>.

5) Where the lines <u>meet</u> is the <u>top of the image</u>.

6) And once you've done all that, <u>do it all again</u> for the bottom of the object.

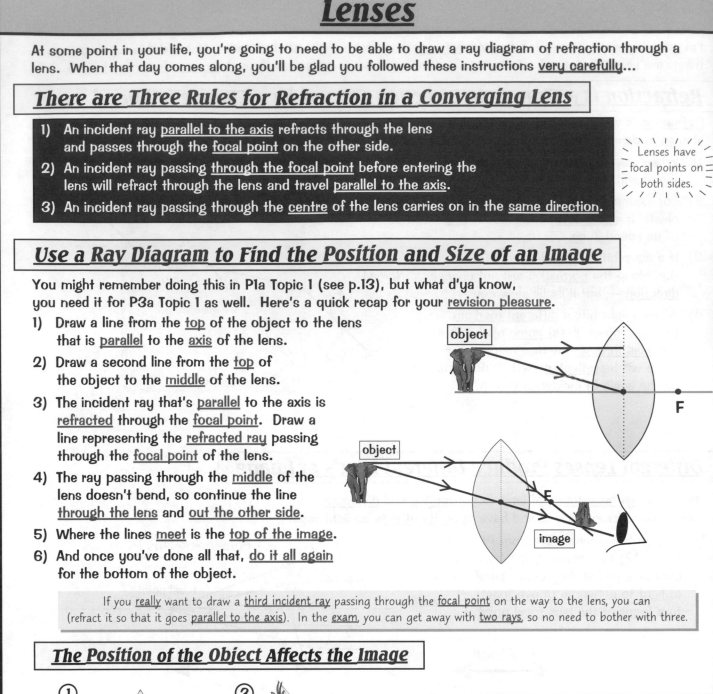

If you <u>really</u> want to draw a <u>third incident ray</u> passing through the <u>focal point</u> on the way to the lens, you can (refract it so that it goes <u>parallel to the axis</u>). In the <u>exam</u>, you can get away with <u>two rays</u>, so no need to bother with three.

The Position of the Object Affects the Image

	①	②	③
Position of object	At 2F	Between F and 2F	Nearer than F
Real or virtual image?	real	real	virtual
Image orientation	inverted	inverted	right way up
Image size	same as object	bigger than object	bigger than object
Image position	at 2F	beyond 2F	same side of the lens as the object

See p.12 for more on virtual and real images.

Some things look better from a distance...

I know, I know, that table isn't very nice, but that's the information you're going to <u>need to know</u> about the joys of converging lenses and images, so make sure you learn it. When it comes to figuring out if the image is real or virtual, just remember — if it can be projected on a screen it is real. If it can't it's virtual. Sorted.

Lenses

Another day, another ray... diagram. This time for <u>diverging lenses</u>. There's only one way to learn how to do these really — and that's practice, practice and more practice. Good luck!

There are Three Rules for Refraction in a Diverging Lens

1) An incident ray <u>parallel to the axis</u> refracts through the lens, and travels in line with the <u>focal point</u> (so it appears to have come from the focal point).

2) An incident ray passing <u>towards the focal point</u> refracts through the lens and travels <u>parallel to the axis</u>.

3) An incident ray passing through the <u>centre</u> of the lens carries on in the <u>same direction</u>.

The <u>neat thing</u> about these rules is that they allow you to draw ray diagrams <u>without</u> bending the rays as they go into the lens <u>and</u> as they leave the lens. You can draw the diagrams as if each ray only changes direction <u>once</u>, in the <u>middle of the lens</u>.

Draw a Ray Diagram for an Image Through a Diverging Lens

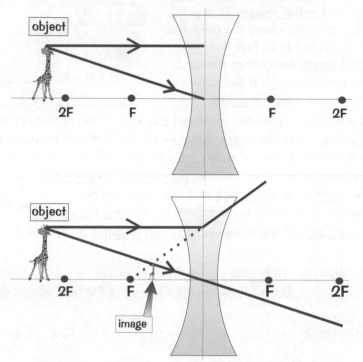

1) Pick a point on the <u>top</u> of the object. Draw a ray going from the object to the lens <u>parallel</u> to the axis of the lens.

2) Draw another ray from the top of the object going right through the middle of the lens.

3) The incident ray that's <u>parallel</u> to the axis is <u>refracted</u> so it appears to have come from the <u>focal point</u>. Draw a <u>ray</u> from the focal point. Make it <u>dotted</u> before it reaches the lens.

4) The ray passing through the <u>middle</u> of the lens doesn't bend.

5) Mark where the refracted rays <u>meet</u>. That's the top of the image.

6) Repeat the process for a point on the bottom of the object. When the bottom of the object is on the <u>axis</u>, the bottom of the image is <u>also</u> on the axis.

Again, if you <u>really</u> want to draw a <u>third incident ray</u> in the direction of the <u>focal point</u> on the far side of the lens, you can. Remember to refract it so that it goes <u>parallel to the axis</u>. In the <u>exam</u>, you can get away with <u>two rays</u>. Choose whichever two are easiest to draw — don't try to draw a ray that won't actually pass through the lens.

The Image is Always Virtual

1) A diverging lens always produces a <u>virtual image</u> (see p.12).

2) The image is <u>right way up</u>, <u>smaller</u> than the object and on the <u>same side of the lens as the object</u> — <u>no matter where the object is</u>.

Virtual giraffes — a bit on the small side...

The tricky part here is remembering that the diverging ray acts as if it's come from the focal point on the <u>same side</u> as the image — get your head round that and your diverging lens ray diagrams will be <u>fabulous</u>. Always draw ray diagrams with a ruler — wiggly lines don't help one bit when you're trying to figure out where the image is.

Power and the Lens Equation

You wanna know just how <u>powerful</u> a <u>lens</u> is? Well it's all explained below...

A Powerful Lens has a Short Focal Length

1) Focal length is related to <u>power</u>. The more <u>powerful</u> the lens, the more <u>strongly</u> it converges rays of light, so the <u>shorter the focal length</u>.

$$\text{Power of lens} \ = \ \frac{1}{\text{Focal length}}$$

E.g. for a lens with focal length f = 0.2 m, power = 1 ÷ 0.2 = 5 D.
(D stands for dioptres, the unit for lens power.)

2) The <u>power</u> of a <u>converging lens</u> is always <u>positive</u>. The <u>power</u> of a <u>diverging lens</u> is always <u>negative</u>.

3) To make a <u>more powerful</u> lens from a certain material, e.g. glass, you just have to make it with more <u>strongly curved surfaces</u>. The power of the lens depends on its <u>shape</u>.

The Lens Equation Works for Converging Lenses

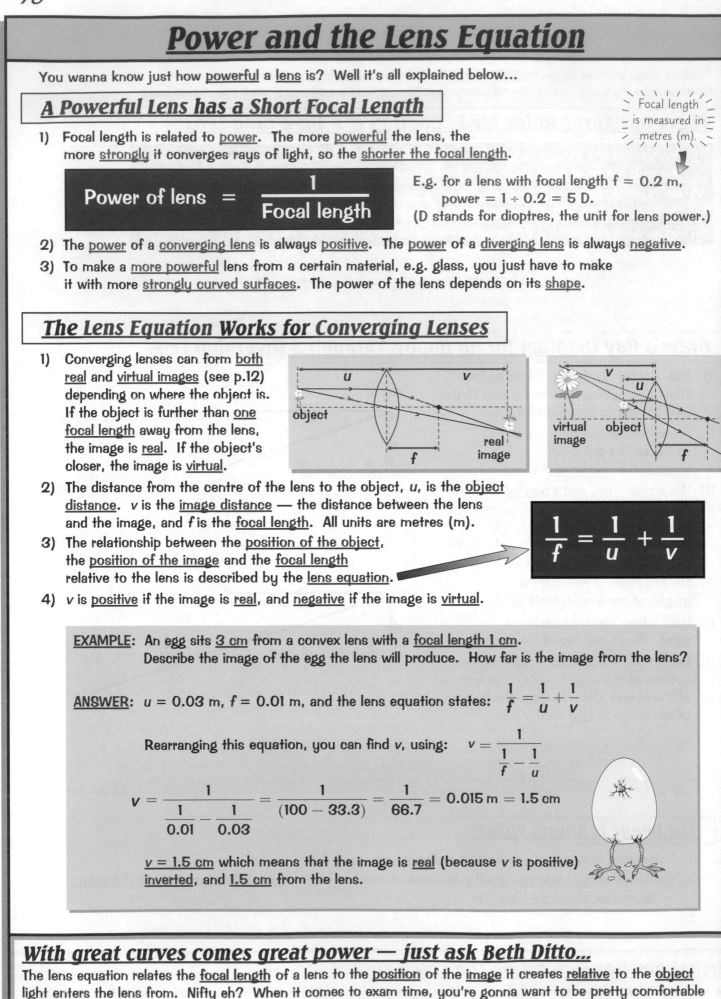

1) Converging lenses can form <u>both</u> <u>real</u> and <u>virtual images</u> (see p.12) depending on where the object is. If the object is further than <u>one focal length</u> away from the lens, the image is <u>real</u>. If the object's closer, the image is <u>virtual</u>.

2) The distance from the centre of the lens to the object, u, is the <u>object distance</u>. v is the <u>image distance</u> — the distance between the lens and the image, and f is the <u>focal length</u>. All units are metres (m).

3) The relationship between the <u>position of the object</u>, the <u>position of the image</u> and the <u>focal length</u> relative to the lens is described by the <u>lens equation</u>.

$$\frac{1}{f} = \frac{1}{u} + \frac{1}{v}$$

4) v is <u>positive</u> if the image is <u>real</u>, and <u>negative</u> if the image is <u>virtual</u>.

EXAMPLE: An egg sits <u>3 cm</u> from a convex lens with a <u>focal length 1 cm</u>. Describe the image of the egg the lens will produce. How far is the image from the lens?

ANSWER: $u = 0.03$ m, $f = 0.01$ m, and the lens equation states: $\frac{1}{f} = \frac{1}{u} + \frac{1}{v}$

Rearranging this equation, you can find v, using: $v = \dfrac{1}{\dfrac{1}{f} - \dfrac{1}{u}}$

$$v = \frac{1}{\dfrac{1}{0.01} - \dfrac{1}{0.03}} = \frac{1}{(100 - 33.3)} = \frac{1}{66.7} = 0.015 \text{ m} = 1.5 \text{ cm}$$

$v = 1.5$ cm which means that the image is <u>real</u> (because v is positive) <u>inverted</u>, and <u>1.5 cm</u> from the lens.

With great curves comes great power — just ask Beth Ditto...

The lens equation relates the <u>focal length</u> of a lens to the <u>position</u> of the <u>image</u> it creates <u>relative</u> to the <u>object</u> light enters the lens from. Nifty eh? When it comes to exam time, you're gonna want to be pretty comfortable with that equation, and with interpreting the numbers that you get out at the end of it. Remember that whether v is <u>positive</u> or <u>negative</u> is important — it tells you whether the image that you see is <u>real</u> or <u>virtual</u>.

The Eye

The eye is an absolute marvel of evolution — the way all the different parts work together to form an image is quite astonishing — bewildering in its beauty and intricacy... Well I like it anyway.

You Need to Know the Basic Structure of the Eye

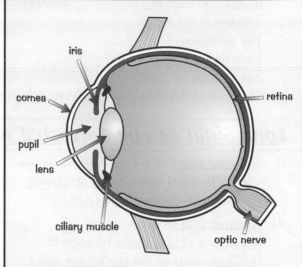

1) The iris is the coloured part of the eye.
   It's made up of muscles that control the size
   of the pupil — the hole in the middle of the iris.
   This controls the amount of light entering the eye.

2) The cornea is a transparent 'window' with a
   convex shape, it does most of the eye's focusing.

3) Light is focused on the retina by the lens and cornea
   working together. The cornea has a fixed power, but the
   lens can change its focusing power by changing shape.

4) The lens is controlled by the ciliary muscles —
   when the ciliary muscles contract, the lens takes
   on a fat, more spherical shape. When they relax
   the lens becomes a thin, flatter shape.

5) The retina is covered in light-sensitive cells which detect
   light and send signals to the brain via the optic nerve.

The Eye has Near and Far Points

1) The far point is the furthest distance that the eye can focus comfortably.

2) For normally-sighted people that's infinity, i.e. you can focus on all distant objects.

3) The near point is the closest distance that the eye can focus on.
   For the average adult that's around 25 cm.

Short Sight and Long Sight are Common Vision Problems

Short-Sighted People can't Focus on Distant Objects

1) Short-sighted people can't focus on objects that are far away
   — this happens if their far point is closer than infinity.

2) Images of distant objects are brought into focus in front of the retina.

3) Short sight can happen for many reasons. The cornea and lens might be too powerful or the
   eyeball is too long. The ciliary muscles might be unable to relax enough to change the shape of
   the lens to focus light on the retina.

Long-Sighted People can't Focus on Things Close Up

1) Long-sighted people can't focus clearly on near objects.
   This happens if their near point is further away than normal (25 cm or more).

2) Images of near objects are brought into focus behind the retina.

3) Long sight might happen because the cornea and lens are too weak or
   the eyeball is too short. The ciliary muscles might not be able to contract enough
   to change the shape of the lens to focus light on the retina.

4) A lot of people become long sighted as they get older because the eye lens becomes stiffer or the
   ciliary muscles become weaker — causing the eye to lose some of its focussing power.

Eyes eyes baby...

The light-sensitive cells in the retina are a collection of rods and cones. Both types of cell send signals up to your
brain, but only the cones (which make up just 5 % of the total number) can see colour. The brain works out all
the different signals, forms an image, puts the image the right way up and figures out what it is. Lovely jubbly.

Correcting Vision Defects

Sometimes things go a little <u>awry</u> in the eye department — and that's when <u>physics</u> steps in to save the day.

Short Sight can be Corrected with Diverging Lenses

1) Glasses with <u>diverging lenses</u> can help to improve <u>short sight</u>.

2) The correcting lens must have its <u>focal point</u> at the eye's <u>faulty far point</u>.

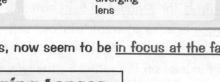

3) This means that objects at infinity, which were out of focus, now seem to be <u>in focus at the far point</u> (p.79)

Long Sight can be Corrected with Converging Lenses

1) The <u>near point</u> of a long-sighted person can be brought down to <u>25 cm</u> using glasses with <u>converging lenses</u>.

2) A <u>converging lens</u> is used to produce a <u>virtual image</u> of objects <u>0.25 m</u> away at the <u>eye's near point</u>.

3) This means that close objects, which were out of focus, now seem to be in focus at the <u>near point</u>.

Many young children are long-sighted because their lenses have grown quicker than their eyeballs.

Sight can be Corrected with Contact Lenses or Laser Eye Surgery

<u>CONTACT LENSES</u>: The <u>cornea</u> does most of the focussing for the eye, and when it's the <u>wrong shape</u> it can be <u>too weak</u> or too powerful, and can be responsible for both long and short sight. <u>Contact lenses</u> sit on top of the cornea and are shaped to <u>compensate</u> for the fault. Like glasses, contact lenses can be <u>converging</u> or <u>diverging</u>.

<u>LASER EYE SURGERY</u>: Bad eyesight can sometimes be corrected with <u>laser eye surgery</u>. A laser can be used to <u>vaporise tissue</u>, changing the <u>shape</u> of the cornea. <u>Slimming it down</u> makes it <u>less powerful</u> and can improve <u>short sight</u>. <u>Changing the shape</u> so that it's <u>more powerful</u> will improve <u>long sight</u>. The surgeon can <u>precisely</u> control how much tissue the laser takes off, completely correcting the vision.

The Treatment for a Vision Defect Depends on the Patient

Both short and long sight can be corrected with <u>glasses</u>, <u>contact lenses</u> or <u>laser eye surgery</u>.

1) Glasses can be the <u>cheapest option</u>. They can help treat even <u>severe eye problems</u> as you can make very thick lenses if needed. However, some people find them <u>heavy</u> and <u>uncomfortable</u> and don't like the way they <u>look</u>

2) Contact lenses are popular as they're <u>convenient</u>, relatively <u>cheap</u>, <u>lightweight</u> and almost <u>invisible</u>. On the downside, they can be <u>uncomfortable</u> and some times <u>fall out</u> of your eye. They can also cause <u>eye infections</u> if they're not looked after properly.

3) Laser eye surgery has the potential to properly fix your vision so you <u>don't need</u> glasses or contact lenses, but it can be very <u>expensive</u>. Like all <u>surgical procedures</u>, there is a risk of <u>complications</u> — you might get an <u>infection</u>, or your eye could respond unexpectedly, making your sight worse than it was before.

4) Throughout your life, your lenses can <u>change shape</u> and <u>lose their ability to focus</u>. Glasses and contacts can easily be <u>adjusted</u> to correct vision changes. Laser eye surgery <u>permanently</u> changes the cornea, but won't necessarily stop your vision from deteriorating.

Wear glasses — they give you specs appeal..

You won't have to draw those ray diagrams for different lenses in the exam, but you may have to interpret them.

Snell's Law and Total Internal Reflection

So you're totally happy with the last two pages. You're sure? Good. Time for some more refraction then...

Every Transparent Material has a Refractive Index

1) The amount that light is refracted (see p.75) depends on a material's refractive index.

2) Light slows down a lot in glass, so the refractive index of glass is high (around 1.5). The refractive index of water is a bit lower (around 1.33) — so light doesn't slow down as much in water as in glass.

3) The speed of light in air is about the same as in a vacuum, so the refractive index of air is 1 (to 2 d.p.).

4) According to Snell's law, the angle of incidence, angle of refraction and refractive index are all linked...

Snell's Law Says...

When an incident ray passes into a material the angle of incidence, i, angle of refraction, r, and refractive index, n, are related by this formula:

So if you know any two of n, i or r, you can work out the missing one.

(Thankfully you don't have to know why Snell's law works. Just that it does.)

$$n = \frac{\sin i}{\sin r}$$

air (refractive index = 1)

material with refractive index = n

Total Internal Reflection (TIR) Depends on the Angle of Incidence

1) When light leaves a material with a higher refractive index and enters a material with a lower refractive index, it speeds up and so bends away from the normal — e.g. when travelling from glass into air.

2) If you keep increasing the angle of incidence, the angle of refraction gets closer and closer to 90°. Eventually i reaches a critical angle, C, for which r = 90°. The light is refracted right along the boundary. Above this critical angle, you get total internal reflection — no light leaves the medium.

3) You can do experiments to find the critical angle for air/glass or air/perspex boundaries using a semi-circular prism, a beam of light and a protractor...

Draw two lines at right angles to each other on a piece of paper. Put the prism on top of the paper so that the straight edge lines up with one of the lines, with the other line going through the middle of the prism. The line at 90° to the edge of the prism is the normal. Start by shining the light beam from the curved side of the prism along the normal. As you gradually increase the angle of the incidence, the refracted ray will get closer to the straight edge of the prism...

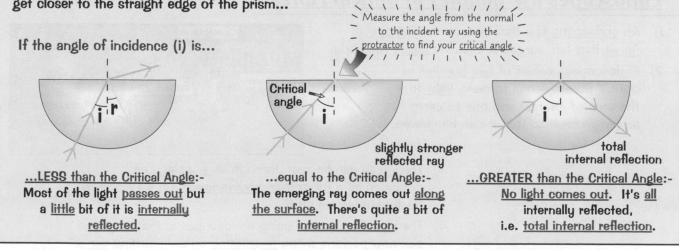

Measure the angle from the normal to the incident ray using the protractor to find your critical angle.

If the angle of incidence (i) is...

...LESS than the Critical Angle:-
Most of the light passes out but a little bit of it is internally reflected.

slightly stronger reflected ray

...equal to the Critical Angle:-
The emerging ray comes out along the surface. There's quite a bit of internal reflection.

total internal reflection

...GREATER than the Critical Angle:-
No light comes out. It's all internally reflected, i.e. total internal reflection.

4) You can investigate the critical angle for a water and air boundary by shining a beam of light up through a rectangular tank. The light will totally internally reflect at an angle of about 49°.

Snell's law smells...

The refractive index of water is what's responsible for pretty rainbows. All together now, ahhhhhhhhhhhhhhhh.

Uses of Total Internal Reflection

There is a point to all these prisms and ray diagrams — total internal reflection turns out to be really useful...

You can find Critical Angles Using Snell's Law

1) When the incident angle, i, is equal to the critical angle, C (see p.81), the angle of refraction is 90°.

2) Sin 90 = 1, so the right hand side of Snell's law becomes just sin C.

3) So, you can find the critical angle, C, using this equation:

$$\sin C = \frac{n_r}{n_i}$$

n_r is the refractive index of the stuff the light's travelling TOWARDS.

n_i is the refractive index of the material the light starts FROM.

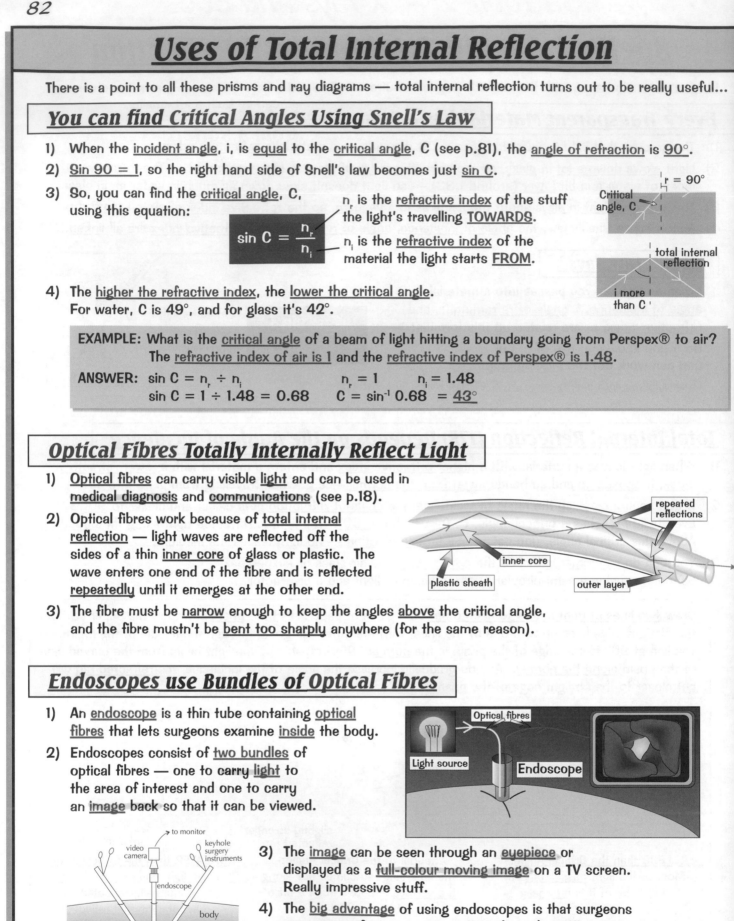

4) The higher the refractive index, the lower the critical angle. For water, C is 49°, and for glass it's 42°.

> EXAMPLE: What is the critical angle of a beam of light hitting a boundary going from Perspex® to air? The refractive index of air is 1 and the refractive index of Perspex® is 1.48.
>
> ANSWER: sin C = $n_r \div n_i$ $n_r = 1$ $n_i = 1.48$
>   sin C = 1 ÷ 1.48 = 0.68   C = $\sin^{-1} 0.68$ = 43°

Optical Fibres Totally Internally Reflect Light

1) Optical fibres can carry visible light and can be used in medical diagnosis and communications (see p.18).

2) Optical fibres work because of total internal reflection — light waves are reflected off the sides of a thin inner core of glass or plastic. The wave enters one end of the fibre and is reflected repeatedly until it emerges at the other end.

3) The fibre must be narrow enough to keep the angles above the critical angle, and the fibre mustn't be bent too sharply anywhere (for the same reason).

Endoscopes use Bundles of Optical Fibres

1) An endoscope is a thin tube containing optical fibres that lets surgeons examine inside the body.

2) Endoscopes consist of two bundles of optical fibres — one to carry light to the area of interest and one to carry an image back so that it can be viewed.

3) The image can be seen through an eyepiece or displayed as a full-colour moving image on a TV screen. Really impressive stuff.

4) The big advantage of using endoscopes is that surgeons can now perform many operations by only cutting eeny weeny holes in people — this is called keyhole surgery, and it wasn't possible before optical fibres.

Internally reflect on this a while...

Sure, endoscopes are useful for medicine, but I use mine to see when dinner's ready from the comfort of my bed..

Electron Beams

Electron beams were used in old-style televisions to produce an image on the screen. Those TVs stuck out so far at the back that they used to fill the room. Nowadays, houses can be built a lot smaller.

Thermionic Emission — Releasing Electrons from a Surface

To produce X-rays (p.15), all you need is a cathode, an anode, an evacuated gas tube and some thermionic emission.

1) A filament acts as a cathode (a negatively charged electrode). The filament is heated which gives more energy to its electrons. Once they have enough energy, they "boil off", i.e. they escape. This process is called thermionic emission.

2) The electrons are then accelerated towards the (positive electrode) anode by a potential difference (voltage) between the cathode and anode.

3) Electron beams can be used to produce X-rays. When the electrons collide with a metal target (the anode), some of their kinetic energy is converted into X-rays.

4) The glass tube contains a vacuum to prevent the electrons colliding with air particles — that would knock them off target and decrease their energy.

5) A lead casing is put around the tube to absorb some of the X-rays so they're only aimed at the thing in question. For example, in hospitals they're aimed at something specific like an arm.

Electrodes are a type of electrical conductor.

Diagram labels: High potential difference; Hot filament (cathode); -ve ┤├ +ve; Evacuated glass tube (a vacuum); Lead casing; electrons emitted; Anode (metal target); X-rays emitted by anode

You Can Calculate the Kinetic Energy of Each Electron...

The kinetic energy gained by each electron as it accelerates is given by:

> **kinetic energy** = **electronic charge (e)** × **accelerating potential difference (V)**
> (in joules, J)   (in coulombs, C)   (in volts, V)

Remember that the kinetic energy of something can be worked out if you know its mass (m) and velocity (v), see page 61.

$$KE = \tfrac{1}{2} \times m \times v^2 = e \times V$$

$$\frac{KE}{e \times V}$$

...and the Size of the Current Produced

The beam of electrons produced is equivalent to an electric current — the same is true for a beam of any charged particles, as current is the rate of flow of charge (p.47). You can calculate the size of this current using the charge on the electron (q) and the number of electrons per second (N) that pass a point, using this equation:

> **Current (I)** = **Number of particles per second (N)** × **Charge on each particle (q)**
> (amperes, A)   (1/second, 1/s)   (coulombs, C)

$$I = N \times q$$

Electron Charge e — An Important Note...

1) The electronic charge, e, is -1.6×10^{-19} coulombs (C). It's a pretty hideous number, so they don't expect you to learn it — they'll give you it in the exam if you need it.

2) Note that the relative charge (see pages 44 and 89) is the charge relative to 1.6×10^{-19} C. That's arranged on purpose, of course, to make the numbers easier: electron –1, proton +1.

3) Relative charge is fine for comparing charges on different particles, but in calculations like the ones above, you need the actual value in coulombs.

What do we want? To emit some electrons! When do want it?

When they're needed, duh. Thanks to thermionic emission, we can produce X-rays whenever the mood takes us. Make sure you know how they're produced and know those pesky equations like the back of your hand.

X-ray Intensity and Absorption

X-rays can be pretty harmful, but we have ways to reduce how much damage they can cause. Ha.
In your face X-rays. In. Your. Face.

X-rays can Harm the Body's Cells Through Ionisation

1) X-rays have a very high frequency and so a high energy (see page 16) —
this means they can be pretty dangerous to us.

2) X-rays have enough energy to be able to ionise molecules in living cells —
removing electrons from atoms, leaving them as positively charged ions.

3) This ionisation means cells might be damaged or destroyed — which can lead to tissue damage or cancer.

Intensity of Radiation Depends on Distance from Source

1) Imagine a source emitting radiation,
e.g. X-rays, next to you. The intensity of
the radiation (see page 74) reaching you
depends on the total area it's spread over.

2) If you move twice as far from the source,
the same radiation is being spread
over four times the area. So you only
receive $\frac{1}{2^2} = \frac{1}{4}$ of the intensity.

3) This is known as an inverse square relationship.

area=A

source of
radiation

area=4A

x   2x

Thickness of Materials Affects X-ray Absorption

1) X-rays are absorbed more by some materials than others — generally, the
more dense a material, the more radiation it absorbs (see page 74).

2) X-ray absorption is also affected by the thickness of the
material through which the X-rays are travelling.

3) The thicker a material, the more X-rays that will be absorbed.

4) Materials like lead and concrete are used to reduce people's exposure to X-rays, e.g. in hospitals.

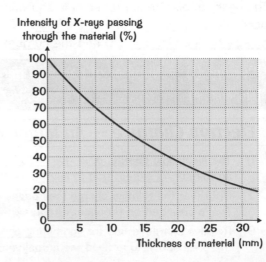

A thick material.

Example: X-ray Tube Casing

1) X-ray tubes (see page 83) have an
outer casing that is used to absorb X-rays.

2) The graph to the right shows an example of how the
intensity of X-rays passing through a material used for
the casing, e.g. lead, depends on how thick it is.

3) The graph shows that the thicker the material, the greater
the reduction in X-ray intensity passing out the other side
of the material — i.e. the more X-rays that are absorbed.

Intensity of X-rays passing
through the material (%)

Thickness of material (mm)

My denseness affects my absorption of information...

I bet you've never seen the words "X-rays" and "absorbs" before as much as you have on this page. That should
be a pretty big hint that you need to know about... well... X-rays and what affects their absorption. Hint, hint.

X-ray Imaging

Weloomo to a pago about <u>fluoroooopy</u> and <u>CAT ooano</u>. What's that? You were expecting a page on X-ray imaging? Well, they are types of X-ray imaging my friend — those X-rays are very <u>versatile</u>.

Fluoroscopes use X-rays to Create Moving Images of Patients' Insides

Moving images of the <u>inside</u> of a patient can be created by using <u>X-ray fluoroscopy</u>.

1) Basic <u>fluoroscopy</u> works by placing a patient <u>between</u> an <u>X-ray source</u> and a <u>fluorescent screen</u>. <u>Different amounts</u> of X-rays are <u>absorbed</u> as they pass through the patient's body (p.74). The <u>intensity</u> of X-rays will <u>vary</u> depending on <u>what</u> they've passed through in the body.

2) The X-rays then hit a <u>fluorescent screen</u> which <u>absorbs</u> them and <u>fluoresces</u> (gives off light) to show a <u>live image</u> on the screen. The image we see is all thanks to the <u>difference</u> in X-ray intensity — exposing the different bits of the screen to <u>different</u> <u>amounts</u> of X-rays. The <u>higher</u> the <u>intensity</u> of the X-rays, the <u>brighter</u> the screen.

3) Modern fluoroscopy now generally involves using an <u>image intensifier</u> to <u>increase</u> the <u>brightness</u> of the <u>image</u> seen (up to 5000 times brighter). This means a <u>lower dose</u> of X-rays can be given to patient.

4) The <u>screen</u> is attached to a <u>computer</u> so the <u>images</u> can be <u>recorded</u>.

5) Fluoroscopy is used to <u>diagnose</u> problems in the way <u>organs</u> are <u>functioning</u>, e.g. looking at <u>movement</u> through the <u>gastrointestinal tract</u> or <u>blood flow</u>. Because X-rays pass <u>easily</u> through <u>soft tissue</u>, the patient is given a '<u>contrast medium</u>' (by injection or ingestion). This is a substance which <u>improves</u> the <u>contrast</u> of the <u>image</u> seen by '<u>enhancing</u>' the <u>soft tissue</u> — making it (and therefore organs) more <u>visible</u>.

CAT Scans Produce Images of 2-D Slices Through the Body

<u>Computerised axial tomography</u> (CAT) scans produce an image of a <u>two-dimensional slice</u> through the body.

1) An X-ray beam <u>rotates</u> around the body and is picked up by thousands of detectors.

2) A computer works out how many of the X-rays are absorbed and produces a very <u>high quality</u> image. This is especially useful for diagnosing less obvious problems.

3) CAT scans can also be used to make <u>three-dimensional</u> <u>images</u> by '<u>stacking</u>' the <u>individual</u> slices.

4) CAT scans are often used to look for <u>tumours</u> and <u>cancer</u>.

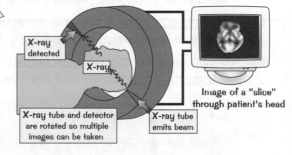

X-ray detected

X-ray

X-ray tube and detector are rotated so multiple images can be taken

X-ray tube emits beam

Image of a "slice" through patient's head

Using X-rays for Imaging and Treatments has Risks and Advantages

1) X-rays can be <u>harmful</u> to us (see page 84). Despite this, they're often still the <u>best choice</u> to <u>treat</u> or <u>diagnose</u> a patient. This is because the <u>benefits</u> of using it usually <u>outweigh</u> the <u>risks</u>.

2) For example, it's better to be able to properly <u>diagnose</u> a patient's injury rather than risk using the <u>wrong treatment</u>.

3) Hospitals try to <u>limit</u> X-ray exposure and <u>reduce risk</u> to the patient (p.93) as much as possible.

4) Using X-rays is a <u>non-invasive</u> procedure — this means the patient <u>doesn't undergo</u> <u>incisions</u> or <u>surgery</u>. This means the procedures are also generally <u>quite quick</u>.

5) Safer <u>non-ionisng</u> radiation techniques are used for <u>imaging</u> and <u>treatment</u> of patients instead of methods that use <u>X-rays</u> where possible, e.g. <u>ultrasound</u> (p.28). The <u>quality</u> of the <u>images</u> taken using this radiation <u>isn't usually as good</u> as X-ray images, and so it's often <u>less useful</u> when diagnosing medical conditions.

CAT scans — I've got a good feline about them...

My word, X-rays have lots of uses. Make sure you know them all. And <u>why</u> X-rays are used despite the <u>risks</u>. semi-interesting fact: images from early fluoroscopes weren't very bright so the radiologists using them had to dapt their eyes by sitting in <u>dark rooms</u> so they could see them. Funnily enough, I often sit in dark rooms too.

Electricity and the Body

We've all seen <u>defibrillators</u> used in films and in TV medical dramas to 'jump-start' someone's heart. So it'd seem that electricity definitely has some kind of role in the body.

Muscle Cells Can Generate Potential Differences

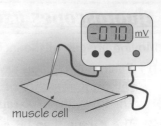

1) Between the <u>inside</u> of a muscle cell and the <u>outside</u>, there's a <u>potential difference</u> (a voltage). The potential difference across the <u>cell membrane</u> of a muscle cell at rest is called the <u>resting potential</u>.

2) These potential differences can be <u>measured</u> with really teeny tiny needle electrodes. The resting potential of a muscle cell is about <u>−70 mV</u> (millivolts).

> When a muscle cell is <u>stimulated</u> by an electrical signal, the <u>potential difference</u> changes from −70 mV to about <u>+40 mV</u>. This increased potential is called an **ACTION POTENTIAL**. The action potential passes down the length of the cell, making the muscle cell <u>contract</u>.

Electrocardiographs Measure the Action Potentials of the Heart

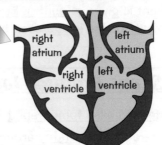

1) The heart is a pump made of <u>muscle</u>, which is split up into <u>four</u> <u>chambers</u> — the <u>atria</u> at the top and the <u>ventricles</u> at the bottom.

2) When the heart <u>beats</u>, an <u>action potential</u> passes through the <u>atria</u>, making them <u>contract</u>. A fraction of a second later, <u>another</u> action potential passes through the <u>ventricles</u>, making them contract too.

3) Once the action potential has passed, the muscle <u>relaxes</u>.

4) These action potentials produce <u>weak electrical signals</u> on the skin.

5) An <u>electrocardiograph</u> records the <u>action potentials</u> of the heart using electrodes stuck onto the chest, arms and legs. For accurate readings the patient should lie or sit still and relax.

6) The results are displayed <u>on a screen</u> or printed out as a <u>graph</u> called an <u>electrocardiogram</u> (ECG), and are used to look at the <u>action</u> of the <u>heart</u>.

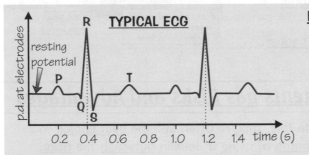

LEARN the <u>basic shape</u> and <u>what it means</u>:
- The horizontal line is just the <u>resting potential</u>.
- The 'blip' at <u>P</u> shows the <u>contraction</u> of the <u>atria</u>.
- The <u>QRS</u> blip shows the <u>contraction</u> of the <u>ventricles</u>. It's a <u>weird shape</u> because you've got the <u>relaxation</u> of the <u>atria</u> going on there too.
- And <u>T</u> shows the <u>relaxation</u> of the <u>ventricles</u>.

7) You can work out the <u>heart rate</u> from an ECG using:

$$\text{frequency (hertz)} = \frac{1}{\text{time period (seconds)}}$$

On the graph, the time from peak to peak is 0.8 seconds. So frequency = 1/0.8 = <u>1.25 Hz</u>. Multiplying by 60 converts this into a <u>heart rate</u> in <u>beats per minute</u>: 1.25 × 60 = <u>75 beats per minute</u>.

Wonder what the average heart rate is during exams...

Plenty of new stuff to learn here. In the exam, they could give you a graph showing an ECG of a normal heart and ask you what each section represents. They could also ask you to work out a heart rate based on an ECG, so don't forget the formula <u>f = 1/T</u>. Remember, the time period (T) is the time from <u>peak</u> to <u>peak</u>. Good-o.

Pacemakers and Pulse Oximeters

My heart skips a beat everytime I see that bloke from that TV show about that thing. But that isn't a medical condition. It's just a big, fat crush. Some actual real-life heart conditions can be helped with a pacemaker...

A Pacemaker is a Device used to Regulate Heart Beat

1) The heart has a natural pacemaker — a group of cells in the wall of the right atrium which produce electrical signals that pulse about 70 times a minute. These signals spread throughout the atria and make them contract via the action potential. The signals then pass on to the ventricles and they contract too (p.86).

2) The heart's natural pacemaker directly controls the heart rate. However, sometimes this natural pacemaker isn't fast enough, or it pulses irregularly, or there are other problems with the electrical signals being sent.

3) People with these kinds of problems may be fitted with an artificial pacemaker — a device that keeps the heart beating steadily using small electric impulses to stimulate the heart to beat.

4) These small electric impulses are sent via electrodes — thin wires attached to the heart.

5) A pacemaker can be fitted with minor surgery and only a small incision needs to be made to insert it. However, artificial pacemakers are powered by batteries, so they will eventually need replacing when the battery loses power.

6) Many modern pacemakers can now be programmed externally — this means the pacemaker's settings can be changed without the patient having to undergo surgery again.

7) Some modern pacemakers are able to monitor things like your breathing and temperature, and then use this information to adjust your heat rate to match whatever activity you're doing.

Pacemakers — not to be confused with... er... pacemakers.

Pulse Oximeters Use Light to Check the % Oxygen in the Blood

Pulse oximetry measures the amount of oxygen carried by the haemoglobin in a patient's blood. This is useful for monitoring the patient's health before and after surgery.

Here's the biology bit:

1) Haemoglobin carries oxygen around your body from your lungs to your cells. Haemoglobin's the pigment which makes your blood red.

2) Haemoglobin changes colour depending on its oxygen content. When it's rich in absorbed oxygen it's bright red in colour (and it's called oxyhaemoglobin). After giving up its oxygen to cells, it appears purply in colour (and it's called reduced haemoglobin).

Here's the physics bit...

1) A pulse oximeter has a transmitter, which emits two beams of red light. It also has a photo detector to measure light.

2) These are placed on either side of a thin part of the body, e.g. a finger or an ear lobe.

3) The beams of light pass through the tissue. On the way, some of the light is absorbed by the blood, reducing the amount of light detected by the detector.

emitters of red and infrared light

detector

display

98%

4) The amount of light absorption depends on the colour of the blood. The colour of the blood depends on its oxyhaemoglobin content. In their arteries, healthy people normally have at least 95% oxyhaemoglobin and no more than 5% reduced haemoglobin.

5) Reflection pulse oximetry uses a similar technique — it reflects light off red blood cells instead of shining light through a part of the body.

Physics really gets my pulse racing...

Some pacemakers are combined with a small defibrillator. Defibrillators pop up on TV and in films lots — the person holding them always shouts "CLEAR" before using them on someone. CGP disclaimer: yelling "CLEAR" doesn't actually have anything to do with how a defibrillator works — so don't go round shouting it at people you know with heart conditions to see if their pacemaker has one. Unless they ask you to, of course.

Revision Summary for P3a Topics 1 & 2

Wow, it seems like a long time since the start of Topic 1. We've come a long way chaps. The real test of whether you've been paying attention is in these questions. You know the drill by now.

1) What is ultrasound? Give details of two medical applications of ultrasound.

2) What's the proper definition of radiation?

3) What two factors affect the intensity of the radiation you receive from a 40 W light bulb?

4)* a) Write down the equation for intensity of radiation. b) The energy from a 1 kW electric bar heater radiates out evenly over a surface of 4 m². Calculate the intensity of the radiation at that surface.

5) Describe the refraction of light by: a) a converging lens, b) a diverging lens.

6) Describe the characteristics of an image formed from light from an object nearer to a converging lens than its focal point, **F**.

7)* Find the power of a lens with a focal length of 0.25 m.

8) Give the lens equation.

9)* An object was placed 0.2 m in front of a converging lens with a focal length of 0.15 m. How far behind the lens was the image formed?

10) Draw a simple sketch of the eye and label the following:
   a) cornea,   b) iris,   c) pupil,   d) lens,   e) retina,   f) ciliary muscles.

11) Explain the symptoms and causes of: a) short sight, b) long sight.

12) What type of lens could be used to correct: a) short sight, b) long sight?

13) Explain how the following can be used to treat short and long sight:
   a) simple lenses,   b) laser correction.

14) Give one advantage and one disadvantage of using laser correction to correct vision.

15)* Write down the Snell's law formula. A beam of light enters a material with i = 30°. It bends so that r = 20°. What is the refractive index of the material?

16) What is total internal reflection?

17)* What is the critical angle of a beam of light hitting the boundary going from glass to air? The refractive index of air is 1 and the refractive index of glass is 1.52.

18) Describe how total internal reflection is used in optical fibres.

19) Explain how X-rays can be produced in an evacuated glass tube using a hot filament, a metal target and a potential difference. Why does the glass tube used have to contain vacuum?

20)* Calculate the kinetic energy gained by an electron accelerated by a voltage of **230 V**. (use $e = 1.6 \times 10^{-19} C$)

21)* Calculate the current produced when 2.5×10^{19} electrons flow past in 1 second.

22) Describe the relationship between how ionising X-rays are to their frequency and energy.

23) Explain how X-rays produce a photograph of a hand.

24) Explain how a CAT scanner is used to produce an image of a 2-D slice through the body.

25) Suggest a reason why X-rays are still used to scan patients despite the risks from using ionising radiation.

26) What's meant by the 'resting potential' of a muscle cell?

27) What's meant by an 'action potential'?

28)* An ECG shows that Karen's heart sends out a strong electrical signal every 0.7 seconds. Calculate Karen's heart rate in beats per minute.

29) What are artificial pacemakers used for?

30) What colour is oxyhaemoglobin? What colour is reduced haemoglobin?

31) Describe how pulse oximetry works.

Particles in Atoms

Another page full of stuff to know. Fab. But panic ye not, some of it should be familiar to you already...

The Number of Protons in an Atom is Equal to the Number of Electrons

Remember, an atom is made up of protons, neutrons and electrons (see page 44 for more).

1) In an atom, the number of protons is equal to the number of electrons.

2) Electrons are really small compared to protons and neutrons. They all have different charges too. Their relative masses and charges are shown in the table.

PARTICLE	RELATIVE MASS	RELATIVE CHARGE
Proton	1	+1
Neutron	1	0
Electron	$\frac{1}{2000}$	-1

Know the Properties of Alpha, Beta and Gamma Radiation

To be honest, you should be on first name terms with alpha (α), beta (β) and gamma (γ) already (see p.64). But there's no harm in looking through the basic facts again, just to make sure you know what's what.

	alpha	beta	gamma
What is it?	A helium nucleus $_2^4$He	An electron $_{-1}^0$e	Electromagnetic radiation
Is it fast or slow, heavy or light?	Slow and heavy	Light and fast	No mass, very fast
Is it ionising?	Strongly ionising	Moderately ionising	Weakly ionising
How penetrating is it and what stops it?	Stopped by paper, skin, etc.	Stopped by thin metal	Stopped by thick lead or very thick concrete

Positron Radiation is Positively Charged Beta Radiation

$_{+1}^0$e

1) The positron is the antiparticle of the electron. This means they're just like electrons — they've got exactly the same relative mass, but their relative charge is +1 (they're positively charged).

2) Positrons have the same properties as electrons — they're light and fast moving, moderately ionising and are stopped by a sheet of thin metal.

3) But positrons are obliterated in spectacular fashion as soon as they meet an electron — this is called annihilation (see p.98).

Neutron Radiation is... Neutrons

$_0^1$n

1) Neutrons are more penetrating than alpha or beta and sometimes even more penetrating than gamma.

2) Unlike alpha, beta and gamma, neutrons aren't directly ionising, but they can be absorbed by the nuclei of atoms in the substances they pass through.

3) Absorbing a neutron can make a nucleus radioactive (p.90).

4) These radioactive nuclei then emit ionising radiation (α, β or γ), so neutrons are sometimes called 'indirectly ionising'.

See page 65 for how neutrons act in nuclear chain reactions.

5) Neutrons are absorbed best by light nuclei. Hydrogen nuclei are the lightest of all, so hydrogen-rich materials such as water, polythene or concrete are used to make neutron radiation shielding.

6) Neutron absorption often makes nuclei emit gamma radiation, so some nice thick lead can be added to neutron radiation shielding, to shield against gamma radiation as well.

Beware the mild-mannered neutron...

Most of the stuff at the top of the page is revision of what you've done before (easy marks if you know it) with some stuff of positrons thrown in. Make sure you know all about the neutron — on one hand it's neutral, doesn't ionise things and can't be easily detected. On the other, it can make things radioactive. Quite a split personality.

Stability and Radioactive Decay

Unstable isotopes emit <u>alpha particles</u>, <u>beta particles</u> or <u>gamma radiation</u> to become more <u>stable</u>.

Some Nuclei are More Stable than Others

A nucleus will be <u>unstable</u> if it has:

1) <u>too many neutrons</u>

2) <u>too few neutrons</u>

3) <u>too many protons and neutrons</u> altogether, i.e. it's <u>too heavy</u>

4) <u>too much energy</u>.

Plot the number of neutrons (N) against the number of protons (Z) for <u>stable isotopes</u> and you get this nice <u>curve of stability</u>.

1) Any isotope which <u>doesn't</u> lie on the curve is <u>unstable</u>.
   Unstable means <u>radioactive</u> — <u>particles</u> or <u>radiation</u> are emitted.

2) An isotope that lies <u>above the curve</u> has <u>too many neutrons</u> to be stable.

3) An isotope that lies <u>below the curve</u> has <u>too few neutrons</u> to be stable.

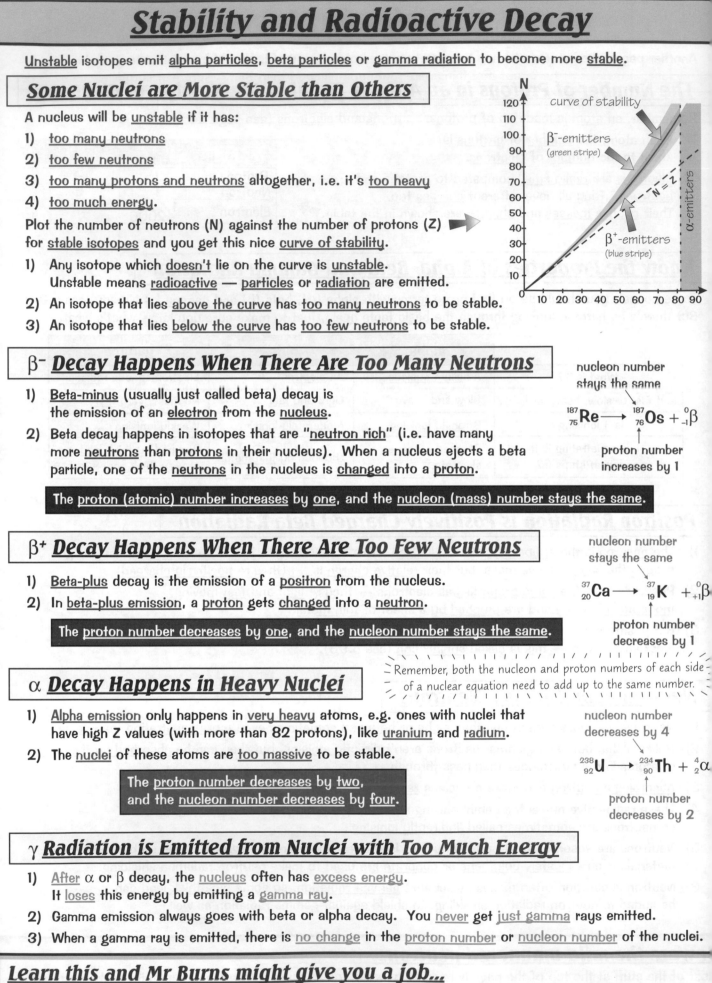

β⁻ Decay Happens When There Are Too Many Neutrons

1) <u>Beta-minus</u> (usually just called beta) decay is the emission of an <u>electron</u> from the <u>nucleus</u>.

2) Beta decay happens in isotopes that are "<u>neutron rich</u>" (i.e. have many more <u>neutrons</u> than <u>protons</u> in their nucleus). When a nucleus ejects a beta particle, one of the <u>neutrons</u> in the nucleus is <u>changed</u> into a <u>proton</u>.

nucleon number stays the same

$$^{187}_{75}\text{Re} \longrightarrow \, ^{187}_{76}\text{Os} + \, ^{0}_{-1}\beta$$

proton number increases by 1

The <u>proton (atomic) number increases</u> by <u>one</u>, and the <u>nucleon (mass) number stays the same</u>.

β⁺ Decay Happens When There Are Too Few Neutrons

1) <u>Beta-plus</u> decay is the emission of a <u>positron</u> from the nucleus.

2) In <u>beta-plus emission</u>, a <u>proton</u> gets <u>changed</u> into a <u>neutron</u>.

nucleon number stays the same

$$^{37}_{20}\text{Ca} \longrightarrow \, ^{37}_{19}\text{K} + \, ^{0}_{+1}\beta$$

proton number decreases by 1

The <u>proton number decreases</u> by <u>one</u>, and the <u>nucleon number stays the same</u>.

α Decay Happens in Heavy Nuclei

Remember, both the nucleon and proton numbers of each side of a nuclear equation need to add up to the same number.

1) <u>Alpha emission</u> only happens in <u>very heavy</u> atoms, e.g. ones with nuclei that have high Z values (with more than 82 protons), like <u>uranium</u> and <u>radium</u>.

2) The <u>nuclei</u> of these atoms are <u>too massive</u> to be stable.

nucleon number decreases by 4

$$^{238}_{92}\text{U} \longrightarrow \, ^{234}_{90}\text{Th} + \, ^{4}_{2}\alpha$$

proton number decreases by 2

The <u>proton number decreases</u> by <u>two</u>, and the <u>nucleon number decreases</u> by <u>four</u>.

γ Radiation is Emitted from Nuclei with Too Much Energy

1) <u>After</u> α or β decay, the <u>nucleus</u> often has <u>excess energy</u>.
   It <u>loses</u> this energy by emitting a <u>gamma ray</u>.

2) Gamma emission always goes with beta or alpha decay. You <u>never</u> get <u>just gamma</u> rays emitted.

3) When a gamma ray is emitted, there is <u>no change</u> in the <u>proton number</u> or <u>nucleon number</u> of the nuclei.

Learn this and Mr Burns might give you a job...

Try it like this: With <u>too many</u> neutrons, you have to <u>take away</u>, so that's <u>beta minus</u>. With <u>too few</u>, you have to <u>add</u> — that's <u>beta-plus</u>. For nuclear equations, balance the top line (mass) <u>AND</u> the bottom line (charge).

Quarks

You'll no doubt be familiar with the basic structure of atoms, with negative electrons orbiting a positive nucleus. However, it turns out that things are more complicated than that... surprise, surprise.

Protons and Neutrons are Made Up of Smaller Particles

1) Protons and neutrons are made up of even smaller particles called quarks.
   It takes three quarks to make a proton or neutron.

2) There are various kinds of quark, but protons and neutrons consist of just two types — up-quarks and down-quarks.

3) The relative charges on up and down quarks are shown in the table.
   When quarks combine to make protons and neutrons, these charges add together to make the overall relative charges.

Quark	Relative Charge	Relative Mass
up	$\frac{2}{3}$	$\frac{1}{3}$
down	$-\frac{1}{3}$	$\frac{1}{3}$

Don't worry about why they're called "up" quarks and "down" quarks. They just are.

A Proton is Made of Two Up-Quarks and One Down-Quark

'up-quark' + 'up-quark' + 'down-quark', so:

charge on proton $= \frac{2}{3} + \frac{2}{3} + \left(-\frac{1}{3}\right) = +1$

mass of proton $= \frac{1}{3} + \frac{1}{3} + \frac{1}{3} = +1$

Remember: protons are 'positive' — they're more 'up' than 'down'.

A Neutron is Made of Two Down-Quarks and One Up-Quark

'up-quark' + 'down-quark' + 'down-quark', so:

charge on neutron $= \frac{2}{3} + \left(-\frac{1}{3}\right) + \left(-\frac{1}{3}\right) = 0$

mass of neutron $= \frac{1}{3} + \frac{1}{3} + \frac{1}{3} = 1$

Quark, quark.

Quarks Change — Producing Electrons/Positrons in the Process

1) Sometimes the number of protons and neutrons in a nucleus can make the nucleus unstable (see p.90).
   To become more stable, a neutron is converted into a proton, or a proton into a neutron.

2) This happens by changing a down-quark into an up-quark, or vice versa.

   Neutron 'up-quark' + 'down-quark' + 'down-quark' ➡ Proton 'up-quark' + 'up-quark' + 'down-quark'

3) However, the overall charge before and after has to be equal.

4) So when a neutron turns into a proton, the nucleus has to produce a negatively charged particle as well to keep the overall charge zero. The particle produced is an electron. This is β⁻ decay.

5) When a proton changes into a neutron (up-quark changes into down-quark), a positive charge is needed to keep the overall charge at +1. The nucleus produces and chucks out a positron. This is β⁺ decay.

My house is like a neutron — one up, two down...

Right then... it's all getting weirder and weirder. So particles can change and become something else, can they — but only if another particle is produced at the same time. Hmm... it all sounds a bit fishy to me. Kind of like saying that a dog can change into a cat, but only if a hamster is produced as well.

Medical Uses of Radiation

Ionising radiation is a bit of a double edged sword. On the one hand, it's scary, harmful stuff, but then it can also really useful in treating and diagnosing illnesses. Read on...

Tracers in Medicine — Always Short Half-Life β or γ-Emitters

Some radioactive isotopes are used as tracers to diagnose some medical conditions.

1) The tracer is injected into the patient or swallowed. An external detector follows its progress as it moves around the body. A computer uses these readings to create an image which shows where the strongest reading of radiation is coming from.

2) A well-known example is the use of iodine-131, which is absorbed by the thyroid gland. It gives out radiation which can be detected to indicate whether the thyroid gland is taking in iodine as it should.

3) Only isotopes which emit beta or gamma are used as they can pass out of the body. They also have short half-lives to reduce the amount of radioactivity inside the patient.

Gamma Rays

G-M tubes Ltd.

Iodine-131 collecting in the thyroid gland

See page 69 for more on tracers.

PET Scanning can Help Diagnose Illnesses

See page 98 for more on PET scans.

Positron emission tomography or PET scanning is a technique used to show tissue or organ function, and can be used to diagnose medical conditions. For example:

1) PET scans show areas of damaged tissue in the heart by detecting areas of decreased blood flow. This can reveal coronary artery disease and damaged or dead heart muscle caused by heart attacks. They can also record blood flow and activity in the brain. This helps diagnose illnesses like epilepsy.

2) PET scans can identify active cancer tumours by showing metabolic activity in tissue. Cancer cells have a much higher metabolism than healthy cells because they're growing like mad.

And here's how it all works — put your best brains in, 'cos this is detailed:

1) Inject the patient with a substance used by the body, e.g. glucose, containing a positron-emitting radioactive isotope with a short half-life so it acts as a tracer, e.g. ^{11}C, ^{13}N, ^{15}O or ^{18}F. Over an hour or so the tracer moves through the body to the organs.

2) Positrons meet electrons and annihilate (see page 98) emitting high-energy gamma rays which are detected. The distribution of radioactivity matches up with metabolic activity. This is because more of the radioactive glucose (or whatever) injected into the patient is taken up and used by cells that are doing more work (cells with an increased metabolism, in other words).

3) The isotopes used in PET scanning have short half-lives, so it's important that they're made close to where they'll be used. Some hospitals have their own cyclotron (see page 95) to make the isotopes on-site. Otherwise, if the isotopes had to be transported over a large distance, their activity could be too low by the time they arrived at the hospital, making them no longer as useful.

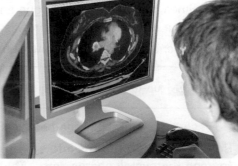

The red region in the chest PET scan above shows a high concentration of radio isotope — this is the location of a cancer tumour.

PET scanning — how they check prices at the pet shop...

PET scans are great because they can show us how the body is functioning. But sadly, they're very expensive — partly because they need the cyclotron close by (see p.95). Not only do cyclotrons take up a lot of energy, the also require a lot of room and some pretty high tech kit, and unfortunately none of that comes cheap.

Medical Uses of Radiation

Right, well that's tracers and PET scanning sorted. I bet you're bursting with anticipation for this page — more medical uses of radiation and some of the drawbacks thrown into the mix too. Crikey.

Radiation can Cause Tissue Damage and Possible Mutations

1) Ionisation caused by radiation can kill a cell completely or damage it so it can't divide — causing tissue damage. Radiation can alter the genetic material in a cell. This can cause mutations. It can also make the cell divide and grow uncontrollably — this is cancer. This is why it's important to limit people's exposure to radiation.

See page 70 for more details.

2) Things like PET scans only use pretty small doses of radiation, e.g. 7 millisieverts (mSv) per PET scan, compared to 2.2 mSv per year background radiation (p.67) from just living in the UK. BUT... ANY exposure to radiation increases the risk of tissue damage and cancer — so it's recommended not to scan patients too often and only if it's necessary. It's all a case of balancing risks (see p.85).

3) For treatments and diagnostic methods, patients should be given the lowest possible doses of radiation and have a short exposure time. They might also wear lead shielding to protect areas not being treated.

4) Medical personnel must also limit their exposure to radiation. The intensity of radiation decreases with distance (p.84), so staff should stand well away from sources or remotely control equipment, e.g. from another room. Intensity also depends on the material it has to travel through, so workers may stand behind lead screens or wear protective lead-lined clothing. Their radiation dose must also be closely monitored.

WARNING: X-RAYS IN PROGRESS

Radiation can be Used Internally or Externally to Treat Tumours

1) With internal radiation therapy, a radioactive material is placed inside the body into or near a tumour. This can be done in many ways, e.g. by injecting or implanting a small amount of radioactive substance. This method gives a high dose of radiation to a small part of the body, so damage to normal tissue surrounding the tumour is limited.

2) Tumours can be treated externally using high-energy X-rays or gamma rays (p.69) aimed at the tumour. The radiation is carefully focused at the tumour, but some damage is still done to surrounding healthy cells.

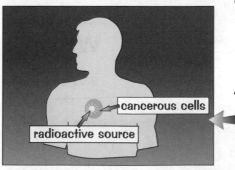

cancerous cells

radioactive source

3) The whole treatment using internal sources is usually shorter than using external sources of radiation — sometimes by up to 6 weeks. This reduces the number of visits a patient has to make to hospital as well as the time they have to wait to undergo any further planned treatment, e.g. chemotherapy.

4) Internal treatments may cause the patient to emit radiation after a source is inserted — so they may have to limit contact with people until it's removed, which in some cases could be several days later. With external sources, each session of the treatment only lasts a few minutes and the patient doesn't emit any radiation afterwards.

5) Internal treatments generally have no side effects, although there may some discomfort from the implant. However, external treatments like radiotherapy can have some short and long term effects (see p.70).

Both are often used alongside other methods to form an effective treatment for cancer.

6) Some uses of internal and external radiation therapy overlap, but they're often used to treat different parts of the body.

Medical tests — I failed the one I took to see whether I had a brain...

There's no doubt about it — the use of radiation is medicine is a complex issue. Learn all the facts and you'll be ready for whatever the examiners can throw at you, swift and agile like a ninja of physics...

Medical Uses of Radiation

This page is all about the ethical issues that <u>doctors</u>, <u>patients</u> and their <u>families</u> have to face when using radiation in medicine — its tricky stuff.

Using Radiation in Medical Physics Raises Social and Ethical Issues

Radiation is both <u>useful</u> and <u>dangerous</u> (see pages 69-70) — we have to think whether the <u>benefits</u> of using it to <u>diagnose</u> or <u>treat</u> an illness, <u>outweigh</u> the associated risks to the <u>patients</u> involved.

1) Even when <u>precautions</u> are taken, using <u>radiation</u> to kill off <u>cancerous cells</u> will always also cause some <u>damage</u> to <u>normal</u> cells — this can lead to <u>side effects</u>. For example, <u>radiotherapy</u> can cause <u>hair loss</u>, <u>sickness</u> and <u>skin irritation</u>. These fairly <u>minor</u> side effects generally only last <u>as long</u> as the treatment.

2) But there are other <u>more serious</u> side effects that may appear <u>months</u> or <u>years</u> after a radiotherapy treatment has ended that could significantly <u>affect</u> someone's life, e.g. <u>bowel damage</u> or <u>infertility</u>.

3) Some people may argue that if someone's <u>quality of life</u> could be seriously <u>reduced</u> after treatment, then it may not be worth undergoing it in the first place. Some people may <u>refuse</u> treatment because of the <u>risk</u> of getting these side effects.

4) In some <u>rare</u> cases, the patient may even develop a <u>second cancer</u> caused by the <u>radiation</u> used to treat their first cancer. But, without the first treatment the person's <u>life expectancy</u> may be dramatically <u>shorter</u>.

5) <u>Radiotherapy</u> doesn't always lead to a <u>cure</u>, but It can often <u>reduce the suffering</u> of a patient who is close to death. Treatment that reduces suffering without curing an illness is called <u>palliative care</u>.

Developing Medical Techniques can be a Controversial Process

1) Some radioactive medical techniques are <u>relatively new</u> in the medical world. That means we don't yet fully understand the <u>long-term</u> benefits and side effects.

2) New techniques are often tested first on cells grown in a lab, then on animals. Once they've been tested on animals and come out OK, they need to be <u>tested on people</u>. There are <u>ethical arguments</u> that go with this:

Some people also argue that it is unethical to test new treatments or drugs on animals.

- A new technique could have <u>harmful side effects</u>. Patients should be <u>aware</u> of possible side effects before agreeing to take part in <u>medical tests</u>. But doctors <u>don't know for sure</u> what all the side effects could be.
- Lots of <u>ill patients</u> might want to get onto a medical trial. But places are limited.
- When a trial seems to show a new technique <u>works</u>, how long should it be before it's offered to <u>everyone</u>?

A lot of issues for you to learn — and some very serious subject matter...

In some ways, this is an odd part of science because there aren't necessarily any <u>right or wrong answers</u> to any of the questions that medical ethics brings up. What you need to be able to do is <u>remember</u> the facts, <u>understand</u> the different arguments, and present your own <u>logical</u> and <u>balanced</u> interpretation. The examiners won't expect you to have one particular opinion, but they will expect you to understand all the issues and be able to back up your arguments. Cover up this page and write yourself a mini essay on medical ethics to see if you've remembered it all.

Cyclotrons

Cyclotrons are one type of <u>particle accelerator</u>. Particle accelerators are devices that accelerate particles. Quelle surprise. But before we get on to cyclotrons, you need to know a little bit about <u>circular motion</u>...

Circular Motion — Velocity is Constantly Changing

1) Velocity is both the speed and direction of an object.

2) If an object is travelling in a circle it is <u>constantly changing direction</u>, which means it's <u>accelerating</u>.

3) This means there <u>must</u> be a <u>resultant force</u> (p.56) acting on it.

4) This force acts towards the centre of the circle.

5) This force that keeps something moving in a circle is called a <u>centripetal force</u>.

It's pronounced sen-tree-pee-tal.

The velocity's in this direction, but...

...the force is always towards the centre of the circle.

Charged Particles are Affected by a Magnetic Field

1) A <u>charged particle</u> in a <u>magnetic field</u> will experience a <u>force</u>. The force on a moving charge in a magnetic field is always <u>perpendicular</u> to its <u>direction</u> of travel — making the <u>particle</u> follow a <u>curved track</u>.

Charged particle

Force on particle

Circular path

Direction of travel

Magnetic field (⊗)

Radius of path decreases as particle loses energy

Two oppositely charged particles in a magnetic field

2) The <u>direction</u> of the <u>force</u> on a particle depends on its <u>charge</u>. The paths of <u>positive</u> and <u>negative</u> particles curve in <u>opposite</u> directions.

3) Usually you don't see neat circular patterns. Instead the particles move in <u>spirals</u> — this is because the particles <u>lose energy</u> and <u>slow down</u> as they <u>interact</u> with other particles.

4) The <u>less</u> energy the particles have, the <u>more curved</u> their path will be.

5) Magnetic fields are used to make charged particles move in a <u>circular</u> or <u>spiral path</u> in <u>particle accelerators</u>, such as <u>cyclotrons</u> (see below).

Did someone say cyclops?

A Cyclotron is a Circular Particle Accelerator

A <u>cyclotron</u> is a <u>particle accelerator</u> which uses a magnetic field to <u>accelerate</u> particles to <u>very high energies</u> along <u>circular</u> paths.

1) The <u>charged</u> particles (e.g. protons) start at the <u>centre</u> of a <u>cyclotron</u>.

2) The cyclotron uses two hollow <u>semicircular electrodes</u> to <u>accelerate</u> the particles across a gap.

3) An <u>alternating potential difference</u> is applied between the electrodes — as the particles are <u>attracted</u> from one side to the other their energy <u>increases</u> (i.e. they are accelerated).

4) A <u>magnetic field</u> is used to keep the <u>particles</u> moving in a <u>circular motion</u>.

5) The <u>magnetic field</u> makes the particles <u>spiral outwards</u> as their <u>energy</u> increases.

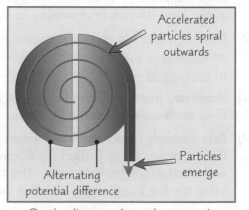

Accelerated particles spiral outwards

Alternating potential difference

Particles emerge

On the diagram above, the magnetic field is perpendicular to the page.

wonder if its a magnetic field that makes my hair ridiculously curly...

ots of information to take in here. The important thing to remember is that in a cyclotron, the path of the harged particles is a spiral thanks to the <u>magnetic field</u>. A cyclotron is one example of a particle accelerator, ut there are lots of different types with lots of interesting uses. More on that coming straight up...

Uses of Particle Accelerators

You can bombard stable nuclei with various different particles to make unstable nuclei.
Depending on what you use, you get different products — a lot of which are used in medicine.

Proton Enrichment Forms Isotopes That Emit Positrons

1) Some radioactive isotopes are produced by bombarding stable elements with protons.

2) A proton is absorbed by the nucleus. This increases its proton number, so you get a new element.

3) A proton needs a lot of energy to be absorbed into the nucleus, so this process takes place in a cyclotron (a circular particle accelerator — see previous page).

4) The radioisotopes made by proton enrichment are usually positron emitters. Remember, a positron is the antiparticle of an electron — same mass, opposite charge (see p.89).

5) Positron emitters are useful in hospitals — they're used in PET scanning. A PET scanner is a rather spiffy device used to monitor blood flow and metabolism — described in glorious detail on p.92.

6) It's important that radioactive isotopes used for PET scanning have a short half-life so that the patient's exposure to radiation is minimised (see page 70 for more on the effects of radiation).

Examples:

Here are three very useful radioisotopes made by proton bombardment, along with equations showing how they're formed. These are all positron emitters, and are all used in PET scanning.

1) Fluorine-18 is made using an isotope of oxygen called oxygen-18. Fluorine-18 has a half-life of just under 2 hours.

$$^{18}_{8}\text{O} + ^{1}_{1}\text{p} \longrightarrow ^{18}_{9}\text{F} + ^{1}_{0}\text{n}$$

2) Carbon-11 is made using nitrogen-14. Carbon-11 has a half-life of about 20 min.

$$^{14}_{7}\text{N} + ^{1}_{1}\text{p} \longrightarrow ^{11}_{6}\text{C} + ^{4}_{2}\text{He}$$

3) Nitrogen-13 is made using oxygen-16. Nitrogen-13 has a half-life of about 10 min.

$$^{16}_{8}\text{O} + ^{1}_{1}\text{p} \longrightarrow ^{13}_{7}\text{N} + ^{4}_{2}\text{He}$$

Particle Accelerators Help Scientists Find Out About the Universe

Particle accelerators aren't just used for medical purposes (see above) — they're also used by scientists to help them find out more about the universe and what it's made up of...

1) Scientists use huge particle accelerators to smash particles into each other at tremendous speeds, to see what happens — what kind of radiation is given off, what new particles are created, etc. This gives clues about how the universe works, so scientists can develop better explanations about the physical world.

2) Research into big scientific questions like particle physics is done internationally. Particle accelerators are so expensive that not every country can afford its own. Also, it's useful to combine the expertise of lots of specialists — most are looking for the same sort of stuff. Sharing ideas is part of science anyway.

3) However, there are sometimes rival groups and projects that are both looking for the same thing — they each want to be the first one to make a discovery.

4) One example of collaborative working is the Large Hadron Collider at Geneva. This accelerator was built by the European Organization for Nuclear Research (known as CERN). This particle accelerator is the largest and most powerful ever built. The scientists at CERN are using it to try and re-create the conditions just after the Big Bang — by colliding two beams of protons head-on at mega fast speeds.

Learn about proton bombardment and enrich your life...

Yes, I'm as confused as you as to why the acronym for European Organization for Nuclear Research is CERN. But some things we just have to accept. Particle accelerators are exciting stuff. Some people were worried when the Large Hadron Collider first began operating that it'd create a black hole and swallow us all up. How wrong they were, unless you're reading this from a black hole of course. In which case, I believed them all along.

Momentum and Kinetic Energy

Ever wondered what happens to <u>momentum</u> when particles collide or get emitted from nuclei... thought not.

Momentum is Always Conserved

See page 59 for more on momentum.

Remember that the momentum of an object is worked out using: | MOMENTUM = MASS × VELOCITY |

1) In any collision or explosion, <u>momentum is conserved</u> (so long as there aren't any external forces acting). This means that the <u>TOTAL MOMENTUM AFTER</u> is <u>EQUAL TO</u> the <u>TOTAL MOMENTUM BEFORE</u>.

2) The three situations that conservation of momentum might crop up in are:

COLLISION: BOUNCING OFF	COLLISION: JOINING TOGETHER	EXPLOSION: SHOT AND RECOIL
This is similar to when a <u>fast-moving neutron</u> hits a nucleus and bounces off again.	This example is similar to when a <u>neutron</u> or a <u>proton</u> <u>collides</u> with an atom and is <u>absorbed</u> into the nucleus.	This is like a particle being <u>emitted</u> from a nucleus. The nucleus <u>recoils</u> like a fired gun.

EXAMPLE: The diagram represents an alpha decay. Find the velocity of the nucleus after the decay.

before   after

$m_1 + m_2 = 146$ $m_1 = 4$ $m_2 = 142$
$v_1 = 0$ km/s $v_2 = -15\,000$ km/s $v_3 = ?$

Momentum before = Momentum after
$$(146 \times 0) = (4 \times -15\,000) + 142v_3$$
$$0 = -60\,000 + 142v_3$$
$$60\,000 = 142v_3$$
$$v_3 = \underline{423 \text{ km/s to the } \underline{right}}$$

Collisions can be Elastic or Inelastic

An <u>elastic</u> collision is one where <u>momentum</u> is <u>conserved</u> and <u>kinetic energy</u> is <u>conserved</u> — i.e. no energy is dissipated (lost) as heat, sound, etc. If a collision is <u>inelastic</u> it means that <u>some</u> of the <u>kinetic energy</u> is <u>converted</u> into <u>other</u> forms during the collision. But <u>momentum</u> is <u>always conserved</u>.

EXAMPLE: A toy lorry (mass 2 kg) travelling at 3 ms⁻¹ crashes into a smaller toy car (mass 800 g), travelling in the same direction at 2 ms⁻¹. The velocity of the lorry after the collision is 2.6 ms⁻¹ in the same direction. Calculate the new velocity of the car and the total kinetic energy before and after the collision.

2 kg
3 ms⁻¹
BEFORE

800 g
2 ms⁻¹

$v = 2.6$ ms⁻¹ $v = ?$
AFTER

Momentum before collision = Momentum after collision
$$(2 \times 3) + (0.8 \times 2) = (2 \times 2.6) + (0.8v)$$
$$2.4 = 0.8v$$
$$v = \underline{3 \text{ ms}^{-1}}$$

Kinetic Energy before = KE of lorry + KE of car
$$= \tfrac{1}{2}mv^2 \text{ (lorry)} + \tfrac{1}{2}mv^2 \text{ (car)}$$
$$= \tfrac{1}{2}(2 \times 3^2) + \tfrac{1}{2}(0.8 \times 2^2)$$
$$= 9 + 1.6 = \underline{10.6 \text{ J}}$$

Kinetic Energy after $= \tfrac{1}{2}(2 \times 2.6^2) + \tfrac{1}{2}(0.8 \times 3^2)$
$$= 6.76 + 3.6 = \underline{10.36 \text{ J}}$$

The difference in the two values is the amount of kinetic energy <u>dissipated</u> as heat or sound, or in damaging the vehicles — so this is an <u>inelastic collision</u>.

A Bouncing Ball is an Example of an Inelastic Collision

1) Drop a <u>ball</u> and it'll <u>bounce</u>. But it <u>won't</u> bounce <u>as high</u> as the height you <u>dropped</u> it from. Remember, when an object <u>falls</u> its <u>gravitational potential energy</u> is transferred into <u>kinetic energy</u> (p.62). When the ball hits the ground it <u>loses</u> some <u>kinetic energy</u>, e.g. as <u>heat/sound</u> — it is an <u>inelastic collision</u>.

2) So obviously if the ball loses K.E. then it'll have <u>less</u> G.P.E too and so <u>won't</u> reach the same <u>height</u>.

3) You can investigate the <u>factors</u> that affect the <u>rebound height</u> of a ball, by <u>changing one</u> of the following (but keeping the rest the <u>same</u>): the ball <u>material</u>, the <u>surface</u> it's dropped on, the <u>initial height</u> of the drop, etc.

Momentum will never be an endangered species — it's always conserved...

o in <u>elastic</u> collisions, momentum and kinetic energy is <u>conserved</u>. In <u>inelastic</u> collisions, <u>only</u> momentum is.

Annihilation and PET Scans

I'll warn you now, you're about to be told below that gamma rays have <u>momentum</u>... even though they <u>don't have any mass</u>. That may make your brain <u>hurt</u>. But don't worry, you don't need to know how and why.

Momentum is Conserved in Positron/Electron Annihilation

Annihilation = complete destruction

1) When a particle meets its antiparticle (its opposite), the result is <u>annihilation</u>. <u>All the mass</u> of both particles is converted into <u>energy</u>, which is given off in the form of <u>gamma rays</u>.

2) When positrons and electrons meet, they tend to collide <u>head on</u> at the same speed and moving in <u>opposite directions</u> (don't ask why, you really don't want to know).

3) The particles have the <u>same mass</u> and <u>opposite velocities</u>, so the total momentum before the collision is <u>zero</u>.

4) Momentum is always conserved, so the gamma rays produced need to have a <u>total momentum of zero</u>.

5) The way that usually happens is that <u>two gamma rays</u> are produced which have the <u>same energy</u> but exactly <u>opposite velocities</u>.

6) In any particle reaction, the <u>total charge after</u> the reaction must <u>equal</u> the <u>total charge before</u> the reaction.

7) The <u>total charge before</u> the <u>electron-positron</u> collision is <u>zero</u> — since the charge on an electron is <u>-1</u>, and the charge on a positron is <u>+1</u>. Gamma rays have no charge so the <u>charge after</u> the collision is also <u>zero</u> — <u>charge</u> is <u>conserved</u>.

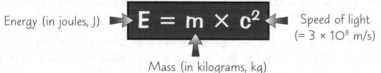

Mass Energy is also Conserved in Positron/Electron Annihilation

1) Einstein said that <u>mass</u> is a <u>form</u> of <u>energy</u> — Mass can be <u>converted</u> into other forms of <u>energy</u> and <u>vice versa</u>. So, you can think of them as being essentially <u>the same thing</u> — <u>mass energy</u>.

2) <u>Mass energy</u> is conserved in <u>annihilation</u> reactions — <u>all</u> the mass of the electron and positron has been converted into <u>energy</u>. It's Einstein's famous equation at work:

Mass to energy, mass to energy, mass to energy...

Energy (in joules, J) → $$E = m \times c^2$$ ← Speed of light (= 3×10^8 m/s)

Mass (in kilograms, kg)

EXAMPLE: Calculate the minimum energy released when an electron and positron annihilate. The mass of an electron or positron is 9.1×10^{-31} kg.

ANSWER: Total mass = $2 \times 9.1 \times 10^{-31} = 1.82 \times 10^{-30}$ kg
$E = 1.82 \times 10^{-30} \times (3 \times 10^8)^2 = \underline{1.638 \times 10^{-13} \text{ J}}$

Since it's the minimum energy, you can ignore the kinetic energy of the particles before they collide.

PET Scanning Involves Positron/Electron Annihilation

(See p.92 for more on PET scanning.)

A positron-emitting <u>radio isotope</u> is injected into a patient. The emitted positrons collide with <u>electrons</u> in the organs, causing them to <u>annihilate</u> and emit <u>high-energy gamma rays</u> (see above). There will be a <u>higher</u> take-up of the radio isotope in <u>tumour cells</u> than in normal cells.

<u>Detectors</u> around the body detect each <u>pair</u> of gamma rays — the <u>tumour</u> will lie along the same path as <u>each pair</u>.

By detecting <u>at least three</u> pairs, the <u>location</u> of the tumour can be <u>accurately</u> found by triangulation (p.31).

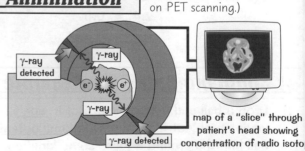

map of a "slice" through patient's head showing concentration of radio isoto

Particle + antiparticle = massive KABOOM...

Remember that in the annihilation of a positron and electron, momentum, charge and mass energy are <u>all</u> conserved. It's pretty weird, but that's <u>physics</u> for you. Try not to worry too much about it and just remember Einstein's idea that mass and energy can be <u>converted</u> into one another. I tell you what, this is brainy stuff folks

Kinetic Theory and Absolute Zero

Particles in gases, absolute zero and the Kelvin scale of temperature — ooh, sounds like fun...

Kinetic Theory Can Explain the Three States of Matter

The three states of matter are solid (e.g. ice), liquid (e.g. water) and gas (e.g. water vapour). The particles of a particular substance in each state are the same — only the arrangement and energy of the particles are different.

SOLIDS — strong forces of attraction hold the particles close together in a fixed, regular arrangement. The particles don't have much energy so they can only vibrate about their fixed positions.

LIQUIDS — there are weaker forces of attraction between the particles. The particles are close together, but can move past each other, and form irregular arrangements. They have more energy than the particles in a solid — they move in random directions at low speeds.

GASES — There are almost no forces of attraction between the particles. The particles have more energy than those in liquids and solids — they are free to move, and travel in random directions and at high speeds.

Gases are Randomly Moving Particles

1) Kinetic theory says that gases consist of very small particles. Which they do — oxygen consists of oxygen molecules, neon consists of neon atoms, etc.

2) These particles are constantly moving and colliding with each other and with the walls of their container, a bit like moshers in a mosh pit. When they collide, they bounce off each other, or off the walls.

3) The particles hardly take up any space. Most of the gas is empty space.

The audience at the Eat My Soul And Die concert all paused to ponder kinetic theory.

Absolute Zero is as Cold as Stuff Can Get — 0 kelvin

1) If you increase the temperature of something, you give its particles more energy — they move about more quickly or vibrate more. In the same way, if you cool a substance down, you're reducing the kinetic energy of the particles.

2) In theory, the coldest that anything can ever get is -273 °C — this temperature is known as absolute zero. At absolute zero, the particles have as little kinetic energy as it's possible to get — they're pretty much still.

3) Absolute zero is the start of the Kelvin scale of temperature.

4) A temperature change of 1 °C is also a change of 1 kelvin. The two scales are pretty similar — the only difference is where the zero occurs.

5) To convert from degrees Celsius to kelvins, just add 273. And to convert from kelvins to degrees Celsius, just subtract 273.

Absolute zero is actually -273.15 °C, but hardly anyone bothers about the 0.15.

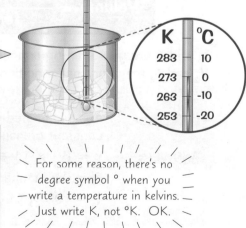

K	°C
283	10
273	0
263	-10
253	-20

For some reason, there's no degree symbol ° when you write a temperature in kelvins. Just write K, not °K. OK.

	Absolute zero	Freezing point of water	Boiling point of water
Celsius scale	-273 °C	0 °C	100 °C
Kelvin scale	0 K	273 K	373 K

Absolute zero — nought, zilch, not a sausage...

Nothing can ever really get to absolute zero (due to some hardcore physics you don't need to know). Scientists have had a bloomin' good go though — so far they've managed to get temperatures down to half a billionth of 1 K. Nice.

Pressure, Volume and Temperature of Gases

Kinetic theory is like backstage at a fashion show — it's full of <u>models</u>. Models describe what goes on at the <u>molecular level</u> in a simple way to make calculations easier. The <u>ideal gas model</u> tells you how gases act...

Kinetic Energy is Proportional to Temperature

The heading makes this sound more complicated than it actually is...

1) If you <u>increase</u> the temperature of a gas, you give its particles <u>more energy</u>.

2) In fact, if you <u>double</u> the temperature (measured in <u>kelvins</u>), you <u>double</u> the average <u>kinetic energy</u> of the particles.

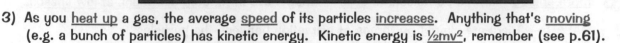

> The <u>Kelvin temperature of a gas</u> is directly proportional to the <u>average kinetic energy</u> of its <u>particles</u>.

3) As you <u>heat up</u> a gas, the average <u>speed</u> of its particles <u>increases</u>. Anything that's <u>moving</u> (e.g. a bunch of particles) has kinetic energy. Kinetic energy is $\frac{1}{2}mv^2$, remember (see p.61).

Kinetic Theory Says Colliding Gas Particles Create Pressure

1) As <u>gas particles</u> move about, they <u>bang into</u> each other and whatever else happens to get in the way.

2) Gas particles are very light, but they sure ain't massless. When they collide with something, they <u>exert a force</u> on it. In a <u>sealed container</u>, gas particles smash against the container's walls — creating an <u>outward pressure</u>.

This all applies to so-called <u>ideal gases</u>. Ideal gases are gases that are '<u>well behaved</u>', i.e. ones that make kinetic theory problems easy to solve... Scientists, eh.

3) This pressure depends on how <u>fast</u> the particles are going and <u>how often</u> they hit the walls.

At Constant Pressure "V/T = Constant"

1) When a gas is at a <u>constant pressure</u>, its <u>volume</u> is <u>proportional</u> to its <u>temperature</u>.

2) What this actually means is that if you have a gas and heat it up you give the particles more <u>kinetic energy</u> and they whizz around faster — the gas <u>expands</u> to take up more room, and so the <u>volume increases</u>.

3) When the pressure is constant, the volume of a gas <u>before</u> a temperature change is related to its volume <u>afterwards</u> by <u>this equation</u>:

At a constant pressure:

$$\text{Volume}_1 = \frac{\text{Volume}_2 \times \text{temperature}_1 \text{(in K)}}{\text{temperature}_2 \text{(in K)}} \quad \longrightarrow \quad V_1 = \frac{V_2 \times T_1}{T_2}$$

V_1 and T_1 are your starting conditions and V_2 and T_2 are your final conditions.

The temperatures in this <u>equation</u> must <u>always</u> be in kelvins, so if they give you the temperatures in °C, convert to kelvins <u>FIRST</u>.

> <u>EXAMPLE:</u> A gas is heated from a temperature of <u>290 K</u> to <u>315 K</u>. Assuming the gas is at a constant pressure, find the initial volume of the gas if the final volume is <u>95 cm³</u>.
>
> <u>ANSWER:</u> $V_1 = (V_2 \times T_1) \div T_2$, $V_2 = 95 \text{ cm}^3$, $T_1 = 290 \text{ K}$, $T_2 = 315 \text{ K}$
> Plug the numbers into the equation:
> $V_1 = (95 \times 290) \div 315 = \underline{87.5 \text{ cm}^3}$ (to 1 d.p.)

Under constant pressure — like me come exam time...

The standard unit of pressure is the <u>pascal</u> (Pa), named after the French scientist Blaise Pascal. One Pa is equal to <u>one newton per square metre</u>, but you'll come across other ways of describing pressure — for example, you might meet the <u>atmosphere</u> (atm), which is the atmospheric pressure at sea level, and is equal to <u>101 325 Pa</u>.

Pressure, Volume and Temperature of Gases

So you know how the temperature and volume change when the pressure is kept the same — sorted. But what about when you've got your gas in a container at a <u>fixed temperature</u>? Don't panic, it's all explained here...

At Constant Temperature, "Pressure × Volume = Constant"

1) In a system where the <u>temperature is constant</u>, reducing the <u>volume</u> of a gas means the particles get <u>more squashed up</u> and hit the walls of the container <u>more often</u>, and the <u>pressure increases</u>.

2) Likewise, if you put the <u>same</u> amount of gas in a <u>bigger</u> container, the <u>pressure will decrease</u>, 'cos there'll be fewer collisions between the gas particles and the container's walls.

3) Pressure and volume are <u>inversely proportional</u> — when volume goes <u>up</u>, pressure goes <u>down</u> (and vice versa).

4) For a gas of <u>fixed mass</u> at a constant temperature, the relationship between volume and pressure is <u>this</u>. Here V_1 and P_1 are the <u>initial</u> volume and pressure, and V_2 and P_2 are the <u>final</u> volume and pressure.

$$V_1 \times P_1 = V_2 \times P_2$$

> **EXAMPLE:** A helium balloon has a volume of <u>7000 cm³</u> and is at a pressure of <u>101 325 Pa</u>. What is the pressure if the balloon is squished to a volume of <u>6000 cm³</u>?
>
> **ANSWER:** $P_2 = (V_1 \times P_1) \div V_2$
> $P_2 = (7000 \times 101\,325) \div 6000 = \underline{118\,213 \text{ Pa}}$

You can Investigate Ideal Gases using a Gas Syringe

You may well meet a <u>gas syringe</u> in your lab experiments — it's just a special type of syringe designed specifically for <u>collecting</u> and <u>measuring</u> gases. You can use this jazzy piece of kit to investigate <u>ideal gas laws</u>.

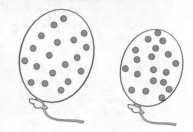
Not an Ideal Gas

Volume and Temperature at a Constant Pressure:

1) Half fill a <u>gas syringe</u> with air and seal it with a rubber bung.

2) Use a Bunsen burner to <u>heat the air</u> in the gas syringe.

3) As it heats up, the gas will <u>expand</u>, pushing the plunger <u>outwards</u> — the <u>volume</u> of the gas will <u>increase</u> as the <u>temperature increases</u>.

4) Since the syringe plunger is <u>free to move</u>, the <u>pressure</u> of the gas <u>stays the same</u>.

5) If you <u>cool it down</u> again, the gas will <u>contract</u>, pulling the plunger <u>in</u> with it.

Pressure and Volume at a Constant Temperature:

1) Attach a <u>gas syringe</u>, half filled with air, to a <u>pressure sensor</u>.

2) If you push the plunger in, you <u>compress</u> the gas and <u>reduce the volume</u>.

3) This <u>increases the gas pressure</u> (because <u>more collisions</u> happen between the particles and the walls).

4) If you pull the plunger out, you <u>increase the volume</u> of the gas and <u>decrease the pressure</u>.

Pressure Sensor

Air

Pressure and volume — what a beautiful relationship...

Heating something up means giving its particles extra <u>kinetic energy</u>, and with an extra kick of K.E. the particles of a gas go bouncing off the walls, just like <u>hyperactive five year-olds</u>. If the pressure is constant, the particles will increase their volume. If the volume is constant, they'll increase their pressure. See? Easy peasy really.

Gas Pressure and Medicine

In General "(P × V)/T = Constant"

Sometimes the pressure and temperature of a gas won't be constant — that's science for you.
Luckily, it's all still pretty straight forward — you just have to use this lovely equation:

$$\frac{\text{pressure} \times \text{volume}}{\text{temperature (in K)}} = \text{constant} \implies \frac{P \times V}{T} = \text{constant} \implies \frac{P_1 V_1}{T_1} = \frac{P_2 V_2}{T_2}$$

EXAMPLE: A gas at a pressure of <u>200 000 Pa</u> is compressed from a volume of <u>0.0003 m³</u> down to a volume of <u>0.000175 m³</u>. During the compression, its temperature increases from <u>230 K</u> to <u>280 K</u>. Find the new pressure of the gas, in Pa.

ANSWER: $P_1 V_1 / T_1 = P_2 V_2 / T_2$ gives: $(200\ 000 \times 0.0003) \div 230 = (P_2 \times 0.000175) \div 280$, so $P_2 \times 0.000175 = [(200\ 000 \times 0.0003) \div 230] \times 280 = 73.04$
$P_2 = 73.04 \div 0.000175 = \underline{417\ 391.3\ \text{Pa}}$

N.B. It's OK to have the volume in cm³ instead of m³, so long as you have the same unit on both sides of the equation. Likewise for pressure — if you're using atm instead of Pa, just make sure that initial and final pressures are in the same units. You need to keep the temperature in kelvins though, otherwise it'll mess everything up. And it's easy enough to convert from °C, just add on 273.

Gases used in Medicine are Kept Under Pressure

1) Many gases are used in medicine, for example, <u>oxygen</u> and <u>nitrogen</u> are needed during operations to help patients breathe. These gases are stored <u>under pressure</u> in metal <u>canisters</u> or <u>bottles</u>.

2) <u>Flow rate</u> is the <u>volume of gas per unit time</u> (seconds, minutes, hours, etc.) released from a gas bottle. Gas canisters are usually fitted with a <u>valve</u> so that the flow rate can be <u>adjusted</u> and <u>controlled</u>.

3) The pressure <u>outside</u> a gas bottle will typically be <u>1 atmosphere</u> (1 atm). Stored gases are kept at a pressure <u>much higher than atmospheric pressure</u> to ensure a <u>high flow rate</u>. Storing at high pressures also means that a <u>lot of gas</u> can be kept in a <u>small volume</u>.

4) The <u>difference</u> in <u>pressure</u> between the <u>inside</u> and <u>outside</u> of a gas bottle is what causes the gas to flow — when the pressures are <u>equal</u>, the gas has no reason to go anywhere. So, a cylinder of gas <u>won't empty completely</u> — once the pressures on the inside and outside are equal, the flow rate will go to <u>zero</u>. This means a volume of gas equal to the volume of the canister will <u>remain inside</u> that canister.

5) <u>Gas canisters</u> need to be made of materials that are <u>strong enough</u> to hold gases under high pressures without buckling or splitting — e.g. <u>steel</u> or <u>carbon reinforced aluminium</u>. The size, materials and pressures used in gas canisters <u>depend</u> on where and what they're used for, e.g. on an <u>ambulance</u> where space is limited, <u>small</u> canisters store gases at <u>very high pressures</u> (to maximise the amount of gas they hold).

EXAMPLE: A <u>1500 cm³</u> bottle of oxygen is stored at a pressure of <u>3.8 atm</u>. The pressure outside the bottle is <u>1 atm</u>. What volume of oxygen is released into the atmosphere if the bottle is opened? Assume that the temperature is constant.

ANSWER: $V_1 = \underline{1500\ \text{cm}^3}$, $P_1 = \underline{3.8\ \text{atm}}$, $P_2 = \underline{1\ \text{atm}}$
The temperature is constant, so $(P_1 \times V_1) = (P_2 \times V_2)$.
Rearranging gives: $V_2 = (P_1 \times V_1) \div P_2 = (3.8 \times 1500) \div 1 = \underline{5700\ \text{cm}^3}$
1500 cm³ will remain inside the bottle (as the pressure difference will be zero).
$V_{\text{released}} = 5700 - 1500 = \underline{4200\ \text{cm}^3}$

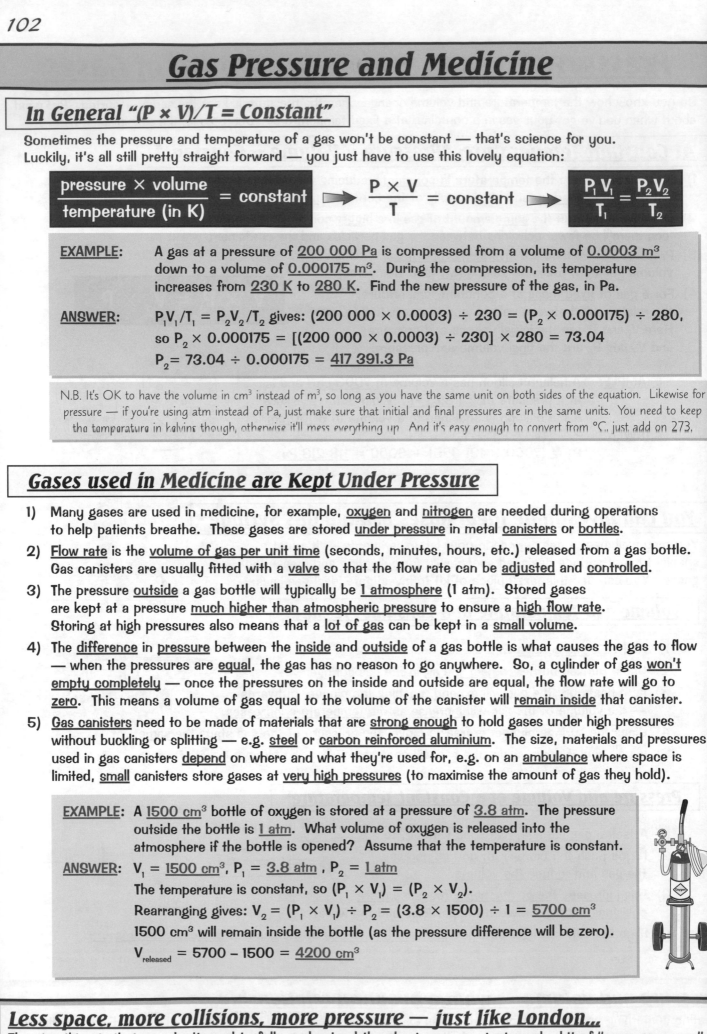

Less space, more collisions, more pressure — just like London...
The nice thing is that you don't need to <u>fully understand</u> the physics — you just need a bit of "common sense" about <u>equations</u>. Understanding always helps of course, but you can still get the right answer without it.

Revision Summary for P3b Topics 3, 4 & 5

Well that's Section 3b done and dusted. What's the best way to celebrate? With some questions I reckon.

1) a) Which is the most ionising out of alpha, beta and gamma radiation?
   b) Which is more ionising out of alpha and positron radiation?
2) Give an example of a good material to use for neutron radiation shielding.
3) Cobalt-60 nuclei lie above the curve of stability.
   a) What does this tell you about the number of neutrons in
      a cobalt-60 nucleus compared to the number of protons?
   b) What kind of particles will cobalt-60 emit?
4) * Uranium-238 is an alpha emitter. Write a nuclear equation
   to show the emission of an alpha particle by uranium-238.
5) Under what conditions is gamma radiation emitted from a nucleus?
6) What particles are neutrons made up from?
7) Add together two up-quarks and a down-quark. What do you get?
8) Describe what happens to the quarks in a neutron during beta-minus decay.
9) Why must an electron be produced when a neutron turns into a proton?
10) What is 'PET' scanning short for? PET scans can detect cancer tumours. Briefly explain how.
11) Why do some radioisotopes used in medicine have to be made in a cyclotron at the hospital itself?
12) Give three ways in which ionising radiation harms cells.
13) Scientists discover a new technique that uses ionising radiation to treat cancer.
    Discuss the issues associated with using and trialling this technique on human patients.
14) A cyclist is moving at a constant speed of 5 m/s around a circular track.
    a) What force keeps the cyclist travelling in a circle?
    b) Where does this force come from?
15) Briefly describe how a cyclotron accelerates particles.
16) What is proton enrichment?
17) Why do scientists want to build massive particle accelerators?
18) Why is it necessary for scientists to collaborate on big projects?
19)* A pink snooker ball travelling at 2 m/s hits a yellow snooker ball travelling
     at 1 m/s in the opposite direction. The pink ball stops. If both snooker
     balls have mass 150 g, what is the new velocity of the yellow ball?
20) a) An electron and a positron travelling at equal speeds but in opposite directions annihilate
        when they collide, producing gamma rays. What is meant by the word 'annihilate'?
    b) How is momentum conserved in this situation?
21) Draw a diagram showing the arrangement of particles in a solid, liquid and gas.
22) What's absolute zero in °C? What does absolute zero mean in terms of the kinetic energy of particles?
23)* Convert the following temperatures into Kelvin: a) -89 °C   b) 120 °C   c) 5 °C
24) How are the temperature of a gas and the average kinetic energy of its particles related?
25) What creates the pressure that a gas exerts on the walls of its container?
26) What two ways are there to increase the pressure of a gas in a sealed container?
27) Give the equation for the relationship between the temperature
    and pressure of a gas in a sealed rigid container.
28) Give the equation for the relationship between temperature, pressure and volume for an ideal gas.
29)* A container of fixed volume 0.0005 m³ is filled with gas at a pressure of 5.0 atm. The container is
     cooled from 25 °C to -100 °C. What will be the new pressure inside the container?
30)* A gas syringe holds 160 cm³ of oxygen at a pressure of 101 325 Pa. The system is kept at a constant
     temperature of 300 K. Calculate the pressure of the gas when compressed to a volume of 40 cm³.
31)* What is the flow rate in cm³/s of a valve that releases all of the available oxygen from a
     2000 cm³ bottle stored at 10 atm into a room at atmospheric pressure in 15 minutes?
     Assume that temperature is constant.

The Perfect Cup of Tea

The making and drinking of tea are important <u>life skills</u>. It's not something that will crop up in the exam, but it is something that will make your <u>revision</u> much <u>easier</u>. So here's a guide to making the <u>perfect cuppa</u>...

1) Choose the Right Mug

A good mug is an <u>essential</u> part of the tea drinking experience, but choosing the <u>right vessel</u> for your tea can be tricky. Here's a guide to choosing your mug:

Some <u>bad</u> mugs:

<u>No</u> handles.

Too <u>fancy</u> (and saucers are for grannies).

Too <u>flimsy</u> and too 80s.

Too many handles.

The <u>perfect</u> mug:

Holds just the <u>right amount</u> of tea.

Wide enough to <u>dunk a biscuit</u>.

Has a <u>design</u> that <u>complements</u> your <u>personality</u> (yoo, I'm a bit hippy).

Nice, <u>easy to hold</u> handle.

2) Get Some Water and Boil It

For a really <u>great brew</u> follow these easy <u>step-by-step</u> instructions:

1) First, pour some <u>water</u> into a <u>kettle</u> and switch it <u>on</u>. (Check it's switched on at the wall too.)

2) Let the kettle <u>boil</u>. While you're waiting, see what's on **TV** later and check your belly button for fluff. Oh, and put a <u>tea bag</u> in a <u>mug</u>.

3) Once the kettle has boiled, <u>pour</u> the water into the mug.

4) <u>Mash</u> the tea bag about a bit with a spoon. <u>Remove</u> the tea bag.

5) Add a splash of <u>milk</u> (and a lump of <u>sugar</u> or two if you're feeling naughty).

Top tea tip no. 23: why not ask your mum if she wants a cup too?

Note: some people may tell you to add the milk <u>before</u> the tea. Scientists have recently confirmed that this is <u>nonsense</u>.

3) Sit Back and Relax

Now this is important — once you've <u>made</u> your cuppa:

1) Have a quick rummage in the kitchen cupboards for a <u>cheeky biscuit</u>. (Custard creams are best — steer clear of any ginger biscuits — they're evil.)

2) Find your favourite <u>armchair/beanbag</u>. Move the <u>cat</u>.

3) Sit back and <u>enjoy</u> your mug of tea. You've <u>earned it</u>.

Phew — time for a brew I reckon...

It's best to <u>ignore</u> what other people say about making cups of tea and follow this method. Trust me, this is the most <u>definitive</u> and <u>effective</u> method. If you don't do it this way, you'll have a <u>shoddy drinking experience</u>. There, you've been warned. Now go and get the kettle on. Mine's milk and two sugars...

Index

Index

Index

Answers

Unit P1a Topic 1 Page 11: $v = f \times \lambda = 2375$ m/s

Revision Summary for P1a Topics 1, 2 & 3 (page 27)

4) 20 m

Revision Summary for P1b Topics 4, 5 & 6 (page 43)

11)

$P = I \times V$

19) a) 2 years
   b) B (payback time is 1.5 years)
   c) $0.1 \times 5 \times 8 = 4p$

25) 70%

Revision Summary for P2a Topics 1, 2 & 3 (page 57)

9) $I = Q \div t$, $t = 10 \times 60 = 600$ s
   $I = 900 \div 600 = 1.5$ A

14) $R = V \div I$, $R = 12 \div 2.5 = 4.8\ \Omega$

17) $I = P \div V$, $I = 1100 \div 230 = 4.8$ A

19) $s = d \div t$, $s = 3.2 \div 35 = 0.091$ m/s
   $d = s \times t$, $d = 0.091 \times (25 \times 60) = 136.5$ m

20) No. speed = distance ÷ time
   speed = $6.3 \div 0.5 = 12.6$ m/s

22) $a = (v - u) \div t$, $a = (14 - 0) \div 0.4 = 35$ m/s^2

32) $F = m \times a$, $a = F \div m$
   $a = 30 \div 4 = 7.5$ m/s^2

Revision Summary for P2b Topics 4, 5 & 6 (page 72)

3) momentum = mass × velocity
   momentum = $78 \times 15 = 1170$ kg m/s

4) $F = (mv - mu) \div t$
   $u = 7$ m/s, $v = 0$ m/s, $m = 50$ kg, $t = 0.5$ s
   $F = (0 - (50 \times 7)) \div 0.5 = -700$ N
   (i.e. 700 N upwards)

7) Work done = force × distance moved in the
   direction of the force
   $E = F \times d = 535 \times 12 = 6420$ J

9) $P = E \div t = 540\,000 \div (4.5 \times 60) = 2000$ W

10) K.E. = ½ × m × v^2 = ½ × 78 × (23^2) = 20 631 J

11) G.P.E. = m × g × h = 12 × 10 × 4.5 = 540 J   (g = 10 N/kg).

12) G.P.E. = m × g × h
   = 15 000 × 10 × 50 = 7 500 000 J (= 7500 kJ)

14) K.E. gained = G.P.E. lost (ignoring air resistance).
   K.E. = m × g × h = 78 × 10 × 20 = 15 600 J (= 15.6 kJ)
   K.E. = ½ × m × v^2
   $v^2 = 2 \times$ K.E. $\div m$
   $v^2 = 2 \times 15\,600 \div 78 = 400$ m/s
   $v = 20$ m/s

29) $840 \div 2 = 420 \rightarrow$ 1 half life
   $420 \div 2 = 210 \rightarrow$ 2 half lives
   $210 \div 2 = 105 \rightarrow$ 3 half lives
   3 half lives pass in 4 hours.
   4 hours = $(4 \times 60) = 240$ mins.
   1 half life = $240 \div 3 = 80$ mins.

Revision Summary for P3a Topics 1 & 2 (page 88)

4) a) Intensity = power ÷ area
   b) Intensity = power ÷ area
   = $1000 \div 4 = 250$ W/m^2

7) Power = 1 ÷ focal length = 1 ÷ 0.25 = 4 D

9) $1/f = 1/u + 1/v$
   $1/v = 1/0.15 - 1/0.2 = 1.667$
   so, $v = 0.6$ m

15) $n = \sin i \div \sin r = \sin 30 \div \sin 20 = 1.46$

17) $\sin C = n_r \div n_i$
   $\sin C = 1 \div 1.52 = 0.658$
   so, $C = 41°$

20) KE = e × V = $1.6 \times 10^{-19} \times 230 = 3.7 \times 10^{-17}$ J

21) $I = N \times q = 2.5 \times 10^{19} \times 1.6 \times 10^{-19} = 4$ A

28) frequency = 1 ÷ time period
   = $1 \div 0.7 = 1.43$
   Convert into a heart rate by × 60,
   so, $1.43 \times 60 = 86$ beats per minute

Revision Summary for P3b Topics 3, 4 & 5 (page 103)

4) $^{238}_{92}U \rightarrow {}^{234}_{90}Th + {}^{4}_{2}\alpha$

19) Momentum = mass × velocity
   Take pink snooker ball to be travelling in the
   positive direction.
   momentum before = momentum after
   $(150 \times 2) + (150 \times -1) = (150 \times 0) + 150V_Y$
   $300 - 150 = 150\ V_Y$
   $150 = 150V_Y$
   $V_Y = 1$ m/s (in positive direction)

23) a) 184 K
   b) 393 K
   c) 278 K

29) $(P_1 \times V_1) \div T_1 = (P_2 \times V_2) \div T_2$
   Volume remains constant: $V_1 = V_2$ so these can
   be cancelled from the equation to get:
   $P_1 \div T_1 = P_2 \div T_2$
   Rearranged: $P_2 = (P_1 \times T_2) \div T_1$
   $P_1 = 5.0$ atm,
   $T_1 = 25\ °C = 298$ K, $T_2 -100\ °C = 173$ K
   $P_2 = (5.0 \times 173) \div 298 = 2.9$ atm

30) $V_1 \times P_1 = V_2 \times P_2$
   $P_2 = (V_1 \times P_1) \div V_2$
   $P_2 = (160 \times 101\,325) \div 40 = 405\,300$ Pa

31) Flow rate = volume out ÷ time
   Volume out = final volume – volume left in bottle
   $V_1 \times P_1 = V_2 \times P_2$
   $V_2 = (V_1 \times P_1) \div P_2$
   $V_1 = 2000$ cm^3, $P_1 = 10$ atm, $P_2 = 1$ atm
   $V_2 = (2000 \times 10) \div 1 = 20\,000$ cm^3
   $V_{out} = V_2 - V_1$
   $V_{out} = 20\,000 - 2000 = 18\,000$ cm^3
   time = 15 mins = $15 \times 60 = 900$ s
   Flow rate = $18\,000 \div 900 = 20$ cm^3/s